The
Changing
Mind

John Roddam

The Changing Mind

With a Foreword by
Sir Julian Huxley, F.R.S.

Little, Brown and Company
Boston · Toronto

Contents

Acknowledgments

I am deeply indebted to Sir Julian Huxley, F.R.S., Professor Roger Masters of Yale and Professor Martin Pollock, F.R.S., of Edinburgh University for the time and trouble they took reading this book in manuscript, and making detailed and general criticisms which were of inestimable value.

I should, however, like to make it quite clear that any errors of omission or commission that remain are of my own making, and that I alone am answerable for the views expressed, the arguments developed and the conclusions reached.

Foreword

MR RODDAM HAS WRITTEN an interesting and stimulating book about the evolutionary process as it has worked itself out so far on this planet from sub-atomic particle to civilized man. He has, moreover, attempted to draw inferences from this total fund of knowledge which is, in this century, for the first time at our disposal.

What Darwin rightly called improvement in evolution has led to an increasing development of 'mind', its capacities for remembering, feeling and willing in animal organisms. This means an increasingly efficient organization of awareness, correlated with the evolution of improved and more elaborate sense-organs and brains.

Man represents the latest term in this trend. When we survey the course of evolution in time we find that there has been a succession of dominant groups. Each new dominant group has originated from a previous one and is successful by reason of some major improvement in biological organization. Man is the latest dominant group and his striking evolutionary success is based entirely on his improved brain and mind. Rational and imaginative conceptual thought and true speech based on learnt symbols has been the result. With these instruments he has achieved something entirely new in the history of this planet—the ability to store experience and transmit it cumulatively from generation to generation, resulting in a second system of heredity by tradition.

Indeed the whole evolutionary process can be seen to fall into three main sectors. The first is the inorganic sector, which resulted in the evolution of elements, nebulae, stars and planetary systems; the second is the organic sector, operating by natural selection and resulting in the evolution of plant and animal organisms; the third is the human or psychosocial sector, operating by mind-accompanied psychosocial pressure superposed upon natural selection and resulting in human societies and their material and cultural products. Man is thus a new and unique *kind* of organism and we must think of the future of man in the terms of psychosocial or cultural evolution.

We can now obtain a general view of the whole evolutionary process. This is the theme of Mr Roddam's book—to point out that such a comprehensive picture can now be drawn and that it is, therefore, essential to make it common knowledge.

This is a beginning. But in addition we can say that man is the only organism capable of achieving further important evolutionary improvement. This is so because major biological evolution came up against a limit in every direction except in that of improved brains and minds, a field which man has pre-empted. Only man has crossed the threshold from the biological into the new psychosocial domain. Having crossed it he has closed the door behind him. What man does is decisive; for the future of the evolutionary process on this planet lies in his hands, whether he knows it or not, whether he wants it or not.

Man is thus presented with a frightening responsibility which is also a challenging opportunity. Mr Roddam has made it his business in the writing of this book to present both the comprehensive evolutionary picture and the challenge to man that it entails.

Man must be made conscious of his and the world's past history so that he may understand himself as both a product and an agent of the evolutionary process, and set himself to explore his own future in the knowledge that the earth is in his charge. Now that we know our place in nature and our evolutionary role, we can begin to plan our destiny.

Today there is a growing realization of these vital matters. Mr Roddam's book is evidence of this, and makes a welcome and useful contribution to the subject.

JULIAN HUXLEY

Preface

THIS IS A book about perspective. Most of us come into the world and pass through and out of it as unaware of the origins of our thoughts, our opinions and our feelings as dogs baying at the moon are unaware of the lunar pull and drag of tidal waters. We need a perspective and a perspective is lying to hand waiting to be noticed, picked up and turned over and to account.

We have for centuries been enjoined to know ourselves. The injunction was well meant, well received and—until recently—inexecutable.

Recently, however, man has been put in and given a perspective by the revelation that there runs throughout nature an undercurrent of change, concealed by its gradualness from our senses. This is evolution: the theory of the continuous change in an irreversible direction of organic and inorganic matter. Our origins have been laid bare, and along with them all the major tortured steps that matter-mind has taken on the way to man, and since his coming.

There is no field of human knowledge that has not contributed its quota to the final synthesis; and every thinker, observer, investigator and research worker pursuing his separate and apparently isolated course in, for example, cosmology, physics, chemistry, biology, zoology, palaeontology, anthropology, history and psychology has found that his field of inquiry has overlapped his neighbours'; as men exploring a new continent from opposite coasts meet eventually face to face in the interior.

Evolution is neither simply an interesting theory of creation, nor a raw, red story of cut-throat competition to survive, to eat, to copulate and re-create. Natural selection is less tolerant of the competitive than of the co-operative, and — what is even more to the point— evolutionary theory reveals what we are mentally and physically; how we became what we are, and what we may yet become. In this century, we are for the first time in history armed with this knowledge, and it is time we bestirred ourselves to take advantage of the fact and ceased playing the roles of pawns in a game of whose rules we can no longer justifiably plead ignorance.

I have tried first to make a survey of the theatre— the cosmos in which the play of forces is being acted out— because it seems to me important that we should see ourselves in the context of our total environment. Then man and all his forerunners, back, back, back to the first neutron are laid, so to speak, on the psycho-analyst's couch so that mind's long case history may be patiently but ruthlessly extracted from them. It is an ambitious undertaking, and I do not doubt that in the course of it errors of omission, errors of detail and over-simplifications of fact and theory have been made. Basically I believe, however, that none of these will by one whit invalidate the argument. The reader is asked to add his own refinements, make his own corrections and pursue the argument graciously, forgiving the imperfections that should be attributed to the prior claims of compression and precision— or to my lack of knowledge.

JOHN RODDAM

The
Changing
Mind

To Nicholas J. Roddam

1 The Stuff of the Universe

THE INKWELL, the snow flake and the frosted window pane; the seascape, the landscape, the tiger and the lily have a fundamental unity, a one-ness, a wholeness, a profound relationship, a basic composition. We and they are made of the same stuff: the stuff of the Universe.

Some 2,500 years ago man first began to wonder whether there did not lie concealed beneath the rich diversity that nature presented to his senses a few indestructible elemental particles of which the whole world of nature was composed. No more fertile concept has surely ever crossed the mind of man. The vibrations it set up have never been stilled for there are few discoveries of science that do not stem from it. Yet the evidences of our senses lay so strong a hand upon us, that it still requires an effort of the imagination to shake ourselves free from them and to unaccustom ourselves to the deception that they so convincingly practise.

When this conjecture was first made there were no means of proving or disproving it. But the brilliantly simple reduction of the Universe to four elements – earth, air, fire and water – although entirely wrong, was magnificently fertile since it set the pace in the right direction: economy of origins.

There are not four, but at least ninety-two elements, ranging from hydrogen, the lightest and simplest, passing by way of the familiar atoms of oxygen, iron, tin, mercury to gold and eventually to uranium, the heaviest and most complex of all. If that were the beginning and the end of the story one might find little to wonder at, for with so surprisingly large a number of basic particles one might expect that the possible molecular combinations would be almost infinite in richness and in number. But this is not so, because the ninety-two 'basic' particles are not basic. They are not the hard, indestructible, granular structures that the Greek imagined. We had to look deeper and further. With the cataloguing of the atoms we had only reached a stage in our search for fundamentals.

Nature does not become simpler the more deeply we probe behind its appearances; it becomes more mysterious. But it also always seems to show economy – economy in the use of raw materials. Perhaps there is only one.

The atoms are divisible, and when they are divided it is discovered that they are all substantially made of the same basic components which are three in number – the proton, the neutron and the electron. These are the bricks with which the entire Universe has been constructed[1], and they differ from each other in two ways only: in mass and in the electrical charges they do or do not carry. The proton is positively and the electron is negatively charged; the neutron carries no charge at all – the differences have beome differences of degree rather than of kind. In exceptional circumstances – by terrestrial standards – they combine, disintegrate and reform. This corps de ballet is the fabric of the Universe, on which and with which we work and hope and think.

The alchemists were right in believing in the possibility of transmuting the elements; only their methods were hopelessly naïve because they had no idea either of the structure of the elements they handled, the vast underworld of the atom, the terrifying power that was locked up in it, or the magnitude of the force needed to make it yield that power.

We ask the scientist to give us a model, and thereby to transpose his incomprehensible mathematical symbols into what is for us reality. The scientist complies while pointing out that the model is only an approximation. He presents us with a world inhabited solely by atoms: atoms compressed, for example, in the complex molecules of the vibrant but hard bone structure of the human body; atoms more loosely assembled in molecules vibrant and jostling in a glass of water; atoms diluted, vibrant and free in the morning mist.

The atoms and molecules are nearer together or further apart according to their environment: in solids, liquid or vapour. But the atom likes its privacy and no matter how cramped its circumstances may appear to be it draws around itself a veil of secrecy: a ring, a field of force. Beneath the veil vibrates and oscillates a thing that for all its unimaginable smallness is itself a composite world of its own.

The sphere of the atom is – to say the least of it – insubstantial. The atom is a void containing an infinitesimal amount of matter, like a pea at large in the City of London. This matter is distributed within the atom rather in the same way as the planets and the sun in the solar system, where the nucleus is the sun and the spinning electrons are the planets. Almost all the weight of the atom is concentrated in the protons and neutrons which form the nucleus. The number of these present in the nucleus and the number of electrons in orbit determine the quality of the element. The difference between oxygen and gold, for example, is just that.

This is the picture we have. It is vastly over-simplified but is basically a valid model.

The sizes, the weights, the speeds of and the forces reposing in the atoms are not comparable with anything with which we are familiar. It is true to say that the more one understands about these particles the less possible it becomes to form any kind of visual picture of them. One has, as it were, to take leave of one's senses. It is natural that it should be so: our senses have never needed and will never need to be aware of the world of the individual atom. It is to their statistical behaviour that they have been conditioned and to which they are admirably attuned. The mind must go on alone without the touchstone of the senses.

It is no easy thing to renounce the possibility of ever having a visual picture—let alone a working model—of the foundations of the Universe on the one hand, and of the cosmos on the other. But there is no way out. For an understanding of the microcosm and the macrocosm our senses are not merely useless they are a handicap. This handicap, apparent though it is when we endeavour to visualize the world of the atom, becomes infinitely more acute when we try to grapple with two other discoveries of this century.

The first is the mass-energy relationship. Energy has mass, and mass has energy. These two apparently fundamentally different manifestations of nature are in fact aspects of the same thing. They are convertible the one into the other and back again. Thus another natural division is broken down, and our sensual analysis of the world into material and immaterial is shown to be invalid. Our senses are again not to blame, for under normal terrestrial conditions the vast temperatures necessary to effect this transformation are never attained. It was with a nuclear weapon that man first achieved this transformation which otherwise takes place only deep within the interiors of the stars.

The second is the analysis of light. How light travels is still a mystery. Of course, it is understood that while sound requires an atmosphere to carry its waves, light has no such need. So that while no sound has ever pierced the vast reaches of interstellar space, light is in no way restricted. It travels, in space, at a uniform velocity of 186,326 miles per second — indefinitely — so that the light that comes to us from the most distant galaxies is 'old' to the tune of 2,000 million years; its life has no end, its journey no destination. The other mystery about light, which even though remaining unsolved we have learnt to come to terms with, is its nature. The problem was to discover whether light is emitted in particles or in waves. The evidence is utterly contradictory and, since it is impossible to reconcile the evidence, the scientist has had to reconcile himself to the fact that light is emitted in *both* ways. Light quanta are, as it were, particles riding on waves. So that we are obliged to abandon another neat category into which we had divided nature.

There is nothing in our experience to enable us to visualize a something that behaves with both the qualities of a particle and the qualities of a wave. It is a fallacy to imagine that it will ever be possible to make a visual description. Man must develop a new sense, or be blindly, gropingly perceptive.

It is very recently — at the beginning of this century — that the physicists led us into this new world out of the mechanistic Universe of the nineteenth century. Planck unknowingly led the way with the Quantum Theory, closely followed by Einstein with the Special and General Theories of Relativity. Planck revealed that energy is not emitted in an even flow, but in definite amounts which he called quanta.

Thus the Universe is no smoothly running affair. It proceeds in jerks like the hands of a clock but, in normal circumstances, the jerks are so close, so small and so fast that they produce the effect of smoothness. Quanta, moreover, for a given frequency, are all exactly alike; all energy is emitted in these discrete amounts.

Einstein's Theory of Relativity is of an entirely different

nature although it utilized Planck's discoveries. Einstein confronts us with a Universe that is devoid of absolutes. We are no longer entitled to measure anything with relationship to a fixed or static body. Objects, space and time are relative— relative to any reference system the observer chooses. The data he obtains by observing, if accurate, can be true for his locality, but it can be true for his locality only. This does not of course, affect the overall order and unity of the Universe, it merely means that there are no absolute standards of measurement which apply simultaneously throughout it. Mass, for example, depends upon the velocity of the moving object, and time depends not only upon the velocity of the clock but of course more generally upon the reference system chosen, i.e., in our case, the diurnal and annual movement of the Earth on its axis and round the Sun. In every case the observer would never notice his changed circumstances since he himself would be affected by it to the same degree as his instruments. It must be realized that there is nothing mechanistic about these changes; they are 'built-in' to the object or clock, quite regardless of its nature or construction.

The Universe that the scientists of the nineteenth century constructed, and which they believed was eventually capable of being completely understood, has disappeared. It was a Universe of machine-like efficiency and predictability. A Universe whose evolution was pre-determined; whose every tick, like an infallible clock, could have been foreseen by an omniscient being at the beginning of time.

The picture has entirely changed. What was determined is unpredictable. What was only matter is also energy. What were only particles are now also waves. What was smoothly running is sporadic and, finally, all the absolutes are relative. There appears to be a fundamental capriciousness underlying the seeming orderliness of nature. Owing to the excessive smallness of the elementary particles we handle them in their billions. We are therefore concerned with their statistical behaviour; with laws of chance and probability. It is as though some giant being to whom men were the size of atoms observed the regular increase /decrease of men/atoms in a great city, which was due to the inflow and outflow by day and night with morning and evening rush hours. The pulsation would be measurable and predictable, but the lives of the individual men/atoms, their birth, death, decay and all the minutiae of their lives would leave unmoved the curving graph of mass behaviour.

Our knowledge of the world above us and the world about us has marched in step. This balanced advance is due to the fact that the Universe throughout its depth is constructed of the same atomic material and is obedient to the same physical laws. So that whether we keep our eyes firmly on the ground or whether we probe the night with the world's most powerful telescope, and look back thousands of millions of years at the distant galaxies, we are looking at members of the same family; all of similar origin, all stuff of the Universe.

All the matter in the Universe is grouped together in vast aggregates of stars and gaseous matter out of which stars are still forming. These aggregates are called galaxies, nebulae or star-clusters. Each contains thousands of millions of stars — with or without accompanying planets — and each is the shape of a great, more or less spherical, disc. When we look at the Milky Way we are looking along the flat disc of our own galaxy, which is average in size, having a diameter of about 100,000 light years.[2]

Galaxies appear to be distributed with remarkable evenness throughout space. The most powerful telescope reveals no thinning out with distance; no empty uninhabited space beyond. Galaxies can be counted in their hundreds of millions, and observing them the astronomer sees the light which set off on its journey long before the first organism on this earth stirred to life.

The origin of the galaxies and the evolutionary stages through which they have passed are still in debate. But all theories have been profoundly influenced by the discovery that the galaxies appear to be receding from one another at speeds proportional to their distances.[3]

The available evidence has led to the existence of three rival theories. The one postulates that if indeed the galaxies are receding from each other at known velocities they must, some time in the remote past — probably 4,000 million years ago — have been clustered together in a vast cloud of gaseous matter. It follows from this theory that in the course of time all the galaxies we now see will pass out of the range of our telescopes, and that our galaxy or cluster of galaxies will be 'alone' in the Universe — which will also incidentally be true of all other galaxies. This will be so no matter how powerful our telescopes become, for since the speed of recession increases with distance, it must eventually exceed the speed of light, with the result that they will be travelling away from us more rapidly than their light will be travelling towards us. This theory leaves much unaccounted for, expecially in so far as the relative abundance and distribution of the elements is concerned.

The second theory assumes that the Universe undergoes cyclical changes: that it pulsates rhythmically over immense periods of time.

The other theory claims that the Universe has always looked and will always look as it is. The galaxies we now see will indeed pass out of sight, but matter in the form of the simplest and most common element, hydrogen, is constantly being created in the intra-galactic void. This matter forms clouds and condenses into new galaxies of stars, in whose hot interiors complex atoms are built up.

This third theory has been received with a considerable amount of favour since it tallies with the cosmic abundance curve, is subject to frequent checks from observation, and integrates nuclear and astrophysical theory.

Transpose this last theory of the expanding Universe on to a backcloth of infinite curved space and time, which had no beginning and can have no end, and one has in one's hands the clearest 'picture' that astronomy and physics can at the moment give without pretence of finality.

The physicist operates first with his imagination and then in the laboratory to put his imaginative concepts to every possible test. His quest has no conceivable end. Discoveries are fertile in nothing so much as in the fresh problems that they disclose. There is no door which science opens which does not reveal another or others beyond it. Our knowledge is not however invalidated by the mysteries that it creates for us. The scientist tells us what he knows and how much more there is to be known. If we were less knowledgable we would be less aware of our ignorance.

2 Planets

MAN'S CURIOSITY ABOUT the nature and origin of the Universe is no new thing; its antiquity is testified by the picturesque accounts that have been handed down to us by all the religions of the world. Each is propounded with the utmost confidence and each contains perhaps a grain of truth: that the entire visible Universe was created out of chaos at a remote date in the past. Creation was regarded as an almost instantaneous event. The concept of evolution is a modern one. Terrestrial — let alone cosmic — change is too slow to make any impression on man's senses.

Moreover, until recently the Universe was thought to be a very small affair, consisting of the Earth, the Moon, the Sun, the planets and the few hundred stars that are visible to the naked eye. All of these objects were believed to be moderate in size and at no great distance. The problem of revealing the nature and origin of this tight little Universe did not appear to be overwhelming.

Our knowledge now is extraordinary and wonderful. Our horizons have been widened to such an extent that their scope defies the imagination. We still do not know how the Universe originated although, as explained in the last chapter, we have highly valuable clues which have narrowed down the possibilities to within manageable proportions.

Nor do we yet know with certainty how the Earth and the

24

other planets of the Sun originated. We do not even know whether the planets are the offspring of stars and that evolutionarily speaking, therefore, they are a later development, or whether the whole solar system came into existence more or less simultaneously.

Nothing would appear more insignificant to a cosmic observer than the cold, small half-lit satellites circling in the retinue of their suns. Yet we know differently. The stars for all their magnificence, apart from illuminating the planets, perform only one other function—they transmute hydrogen in the white-heat of their interiors into the heavy elements of which the Universe stands in need for its growth and diversification. However, when we begin to speak about the planets there is a change of mood. We are on the verge of leaving physics behind and we are standing on the frontiers of biology—of life.

The birth of a planet is the first hesitant step towards the creation of man: man the observer, the recorder and the analyst of the Universe and of himself. It is a fact, perhaps rather a poetic fact, but none the less scientific, that wherever there are planets, amongst them will be found a star—their sun—that sometimes provides them with the means to produce on their surfaces a colossal and utterly unforeseeable variety of living, moving, flowering sentient organisms. The vast majority of planets undoubtedly realize little or nothing of their promise—some, however, do. Stars that have no planets have no history.

How our Sun gave birth to its planets is not yet known with certainty. By and large there are two contending theories. The first supposes that the embryonic Sun in passing through a cloud of cold interstellar gas became greatly extended, and that out of this envelope of gas the planets were formed by condensation. The other theory supposes that the

Sun was a member of what is known as a double-star or binary system.[1] It is further supposed that the Sun's companion was a supernova. Supernovae are very large, highly unstable stars which explode; the recoil from such an explosion—a mere wisp of gas—remains behind within the star's gravitational field, and out of this ring of gas planets eventually condense.[2] Supernovae explosions are spectacular events: three have occurred in our galaxy during the last thousand years.

One fact stands out clearly: no matter which of these theories is eventually proved correct, planetary systems must be very widely and commonly distributed throughout our own and all other galaxies. In the first place, there is still an abundance of interstellar gas in our galaxy despite the passage of some 4,000 million years since stars began to condense out of it, and in the second place, if supernovae explosions occur at the rate of three every thousand years, and half of them occur in binary systems, in our galaxy alone planetary systems would be formed at the rate of $1\frac{1}{2}$ million every 1,000 million years.

It may be that every star has a planetary system. For it may not be necessary to decide which of the above theories of planetary creation is correct. They may be operating simultaneously throughout the Universe.[3] The fact is that the Universe is a very lively place in which a wealth of things are happening. Galaxies are formed out of conglomerates of interstellar gas. Out of the galaxies stars are formed with or without planetary systems, singly, in pairs or even in groups. Some are unstable and explode, others sweep up fresh material on their journeys through space; and out of this swirling incandescent gas satellites are formed, some of which throw off their own satellites and begin a biological cycle. The Universe, for all its cool majestic brilliance, its depth and darkness, is a cauldron of swiftly moving events. Man, with his paltry life span and mind unattuned to cosmic proportions, is always being deceived into perceiving only its changelessness.

Absolute proof does not yet exist. It is therefore wiser to admit that one is speculating on foundations that are not theoretically secure. All the available evidence, however, and the consensus of scientific opinion point in the direction of a multitudinous array of planetary systems. Moreover, it should be recalled that there are some 10,000 million stars in our galaxy alone, and that there are at least 2,000 million other galaxies of a comparable nature. It would be odd indeed if, out of all that, the solar system in general and our Earth in particular were unique.

Telescopes are quite useless as providers of evidence, for planets being both small and non-luminous are invisible. The nearest star—apart, of course, from the Sun—is 25 million million miles away. It may or may not have planets —from here we cannot tell. Even if we go there to find out and even if we travel at half the speed of light—90,000 miles a second—it would take sixteen years to make the return journey.

Therefore the possibility of knowing for certain about the existence of other planets is even by today's standards of progress in space research seemingly out of the question. There remains the possibility that we shall be able to make radio contact with intelligent beings on other planets. This, however, creates a linguistic difficulty which limits the possibility of 'conversation' to the exchange of equations expressed in the symbolism of pure mathematics. Even so there is still the limiting speed of radio waves, which although travelling at the speed of light would entail years of waiting for replies.[4]

The situation is all the more frustrating because the other planets in the solar system are almost certainly uninhabited. Mars appears to have polar ice-caps like our own which spread in the winter and recede in the summer, and there is evidence which suggests seasonal changes in a vegetative covering. Venus has a dense atmosphere which gives it its brilliance but which also makes observation of its surface impossible. However, analysis of its atmosphere reveals that it contains a great deal of carbon dioxide but neither water vapour nor oxygen, which implies a total absence of plant and therefore of animal life. There is no possibility of life having developed on any of the other planets.

It might be thought that perhaps we are taking too narrow — too insular — a view and that, in fact, life of an altogether different kind might have evolved elsewhere; in conditions of extreme (by terrestrial standards) heat or cold, etc., or in the absence of an atmosphere — but this tantalizing possibility must be treated with great reserve since, as we know, the Universe is made throughout of the same stuff. The complex molecules and the proportions of certain elements which have led to the evolution of living organisms on this Planet may be a universal requirement.

It seems more reasonable to suppose that planets are scattered throughout the galaxies in their multitudes like pollen blown by the wind. The vast majority will spin lifelessly through countless ages, unseen, untrodden, silent and dead. On some of them only — but still to be numbered in millions — the temperature, the atmosphere and the presence of certain vital elements wakes a planet into life.

3 Conditions of Life

Nature makes so gradual a transition from the inanimate to the animate kingdom, that the boundary lines which separate them are indistinct and doubtful.

Aristotle

IN THE FIRST two chapters an attempt was made to draw in broad outline the design of the cosmic arena in which as actors and spectators we find ourselves playing out our lives. As science unfolds this design, one alternates between being dwarfed by its magnitude and being magnified and inspired by the fact that mind felt challenged by so great a mystery and has succeeded in resolving so great a part of it. It is, moreover, provocative of thought to consider that the Universe throughout the thousands of millions of years of its existence has, as far as we can tell, never until this precise century bred a mind capable of conceiving it.

That we can conceive it even now is perhaps too proud a boast. The fact is, however, that a coherent picture is developing which can be presented with many reservations, but also with a great deal of confidence, despite the enormous amount of detail that has still to be filled in, and despite the surprises that no doubt lie in store for us.[1]

At this stage it might be as well to recapitulate the evolutionary steps which led to the formation of planets and thus to the creation in certain instances of environments which are congenial to life.

When we probe the very depths of matter (or energy) we find numerous sub-atomic particles, of which the proton, the neutron and the electron appear to be the most important;

29

for they in association form the atoms of which everything in the Universe— without any exception— is composed. Hydrogen is the lightest, the simplest and the most common element, and it is of hydrogen that the vast embryonic nebulae are mainly formed. In time these vast clouds of hydrogen condense into galaxies of stars, and it is deep in the interiors of these stars that sufficiently high temperatures are achieved to enable heavier and more complex atoms to be built up. This process was, and probably still is at work throughout the entire Universe wherever and whenever the raw material— hydrogen— is available.

Stars, analagous to our Sun, are numbered in their thousands of millions in every galaxy. Some or all of these stars, by a process which is not yet fully understood, acquire planets which contain samples in varying proportions of the elements transmuted in the star's interior or in its gravitational field. These planets are not of course self-luminous. Far out in space, dependent upon light and warmth from a distant sun, they begin to fit themselves as possible homes of life.

It is at this juncture that the present chapter takes up the story. The Universe as a whole falls into the background, and attention is concentrated on planets in general, this our Planet in particular, and the steps that lead up to the emergence of life.

Some 4,500 million years ago the Earth, Mars and Venus alone of the nine planets in the solar system swung into orbit between the extremes of heat and cold which inhibit further evolution.

The Earth cooled. It formed a crust. The crust was thin and brittle. It was repeatedly disrupted and reformed. But the cooling continued and so, on balance, the crust thickened. There were earthquakes and volcanoes and unimaginable torrential rains. It was intensely hot and humid. For 2,000

So in those warm primeval oceans, for 2,000 million years of unrecorded history our ancestral atoms moved and joined together, composing patterns—carbohydrates, acids, crystals—achieving ever greater stability and complexity.

In rocks older than 1,000 million years no fossil exists. This, however, is negative and not positive evidence. The frailty of the first cells could not be expected to leave a trace that would endure. Even then the records are vague and unreliable. We cannot speak with certainty about what life was like before 500 million years ago. It is at this date that the next chapter begins.

million years the Earth was the scene of geological and climatic violence: a place of naked rock and steaming seas; of dense atmosphere, pitch black by night, sunless by day. There was no life. Now life is a fine word, and there are few people who have any doubt at all in their minds about what they mean when they use it. They are wrong not to doubt, because the word evades accurate definition. Things that are obviously alive such as giraffes and cauliflowers, and things that are obviously dead such as carpet-slippers and railway stations are very closely related, and the hard distinctions that our common sense presumes are wholly illusory. The animate and the inanimate merge as Aristotle had already divined 2,300 years ago, as the quotation at the beginning of this chapter bears witness. It is time we caught up with him.

There is no intention here to be pedantic. Life is a very useful word, of vital interest and of extreme significance; it is not, however, a scientific classification. The word refers to certain complex structures which have the following attributes: the power to grow, to transform energy, to change their form, to replace old tissue, to reproduce themselves and to react to their environment. The possession of only one of these characteristics, one might say, would entitle anything to lay claim to being alive. However, there is no need to split hairs; some crystals fulfil some of these requirements and yet no one has ever advocated their being numbered among the living.

Where, then, is the frontier? Let us look a little closer into the composition of all those things that are on the fringe. The only materials with which we can construct things animate and inanimate are, of course, atoms. Atoms attract and repel each other. In the former case they coalesce and form molecules such as, to take the most familiar example, a molecule of water—two atoms of hydrogen and one of oxygen—the combination, it should be noted, produces something utterly unforeseeable: neither hydrogen nor oxygen giving the slightest hint in isolation of what they can achieve in combination.

Given that there are ninety-three elements, the possible combinations are clearly almost infinite. Add to this the fact that the results of combining certain atoms may differ considerably according to the pattern they form within the molecule. The definition, therefore, of each molecule depends not only upon the kinds and quantities of atoms that have been used in the construction of it, but also upon the way these atoms have arranged themselves.

Now it is known without any shadow of a doubt that one of the essential classes of substance present in anything that we should call unquestionably animate is protein.

What is protein? Protein is composed of amino-acids. And amino-acids? Amino-acids are combinations of atoms of hydrogen, nitrogen, oxygen and carbon, sometimes with traces of sulphur. The other highly specific macromolecules (nucleic acids, carbohydrates and lipoids) present in most living entities are analogously composed of a limited number of elements strung together in varying patterns.

That is what the living world is made of: the world of leaf and flower and mind and muscle. But let it not be thought that because it is possible to reduce all living things to a few common elements it is simple. For simple above all else it is not.

Amino-acids are limited in number: there are in fact only twenty of any biological significance, and the evolutionary relationships between different species can be traced through the amino-acid arrangements in their proteins. Protein, however, is an aggregate of hundreds, sometimes thousands of amino-acid molecules, and the functional characteristics of

all living things are expressed by the type of proteins they contain.

When it is realized how few and basic are the constituents of living organisms, and yet how complex are their structures two fundamental facts relative to evolution stand out. First there is no frontier between the animate and the inanim We are all made of the same stuff; we are variations theme. Secondly, because of their complexity the m molecules need vast periods of time, in the order evide hundreds of millions of years, in which to develop.

Once we rid our minds of the wholly primitive irrational assumption, fostered by appearances and t that nature is for some reason divided into two living and the dead—we are on the way toward standing of the Universe. This barrier removed free to rove throughout the whole realm of observe the truly marvellous economy by wh sity has been created out of such simplicity. whence we came and we can even retrace countless millennia, through every phas birth and death, over the backwaters evolution, over its successes, its trials an progress and its timid halting advances life was ignorant of its beginning and All this the mind can now encomp first tick of time.

It seems strange now to think th to come round to an acceptance o of nature. One might have tho it even though he could not s trace is lost. Now that we kn that there is less difference be between a newt and a New

4 Ways of Living

WE DEPEND UPON fossils for dating the beginning of recognizable life. But organisms that are capable of leaving fossil remains must be moderately large and immoderately durable; they must also have been numerous and widespread, hence successful. Otherise the chances of finding them are remote. Therefore, if we start our study of life with fossil remains of 500 million years ago, we are like late arrivals at the theatre who miss the first and vital act during which the characters are being built up and the plot is being developed.

The first act in the play of life must, largely by inference, have taken place anterior to fossil remains—before living things had skeletons—during what is known as the Proterozoic Period. The only traces of its multitudinous and simple occupants lie embedded either in marble—the metamorphosed limestone deposits of micro-organisms which may have lived up to 1,000 million years ago—or as carbon in the graphite layers of a corresponding antiquity. Protein is fifty per cent carbon. These graphite layers are therefore in all probability the cemeteries of countless millions of primitive organisms.

The beginnings of life are in some ways life's most interesting feature, for it is they that explored the possibilities and decided upon the pattern. We are still pursuing the ways of living, growing and reproducing that were pioneered by

35

organisms that are too small to be seen with the naked eye. All living things, extinct and contemporary, have their roots in those marble deposits and graphite layers of long ago. This chapter sketches in the briefest outline their ways of living, of feeding and reproducing that were tested and discarded or handed on.

It should not be supposed that a simple straightforward 'ladder of life' can be exposed that leads from the lowest rung of primitive, single-celled animals and plants to the topmost rung of man; a ladder whose each rung represents the arrival or development of a more complex organism, which by virtue of some special and novel quality renders it superior to or makes extinct the rung below. Many of the rungs are missing it is true, and the only evidence for their having existed lies in the fossils they left in passing. At the beginning of the ladder, however, there were no casualties. Simplicity is no disadvantage in the struggle to perpetuate a species. Complexity is the most dangerous path to tread; it leads to dominion or to death, usually death. It is the humble that inherited and still inherit the earth — at least from their point of view, if they have one. Man is merely an incident who is numerically insignificant and a new arrival in comparison with the multitudes and the longevity of the simplest organisms.

Size, complexity, specialization, versatility are ways of living which are fraught with danger. The great explosion of life along these roads, of which man is the result, is outlined in the next chapter; it will bear this point out.

Many of the humbler organisms which preceded this explosion are with us still. Thus we are able to study them as they were and as they are. It enables us to photograph them, to breed them, to place them under the microscope and so to observe and explore all the experiments that they made in ways of living. Thus our understanding of the processes which were selected by the higher forms of life grows by studying the results achieved by those pioneers.

The illusion that there is a great gulf fixed between living and non-living matter—which it is hoped was shattered in the last chapter—is rivalled by another illusion: that plants and animals are quite separate categories of life. This is not so.

It is not really surprising. There are no clear-cut divisions in nature. There is absolutely no reason why there should be. The tide of evolution runs straight through the tidy, finicky classifications in which man tries to contain it. Animals and plants are derived from common ancestors and the edge between these two branches of life is very fuzzy indeed. This fact makes it quite impossible when dealing with many primitive organisms to decide to which branch they belong.

Since this chapter is devoted mainly to a study of these fringe organisms, it is as well at the outset to enumerate the generally accepted differences between plants and animals. There are three.

Firstly, dietic: plant cells produce a substance known as chlorophyll which enables them by a process known as photosynthesis, to nourish themselves on a diet of carbon dioxide with the aid of energy absorbed from sunlight. Animals on the other hand have no chlorophyll in their cells and therefore cannot nourish themselves in this way. They require a richer diet of protein, carbohydrates and fats, made available to them thanks to the 'donkey work' performed by plants. From the plant's point of view animals are parasites.

Secondly, structural: plants are diffuse and rooted to the earth. They need to present the largest possible surface to sun and air, and they do so by means of stem or trunk, by branch and twig and leaf above ground, and below it by ramifications of root. Animals on the contrary are compact of build and free in movement. They have to be 'loose' so that they may go in search of a living.

Thirdly, anatomical: the cell walls of plants are composed of the carbohydrate cellulose, in addition to the membranes which like those of animals are mainly of fats and proteins.

The first two, diet and structure, are very obvious differences which are immediately recognizable in highly developed members of either group. Many simple organisms, however possess the characteristics of plants and animals. Not only, however, can these organisms not make up their minds into which category to fall, but they are also frequently in a sexual quandary, being unable to decide finally upon the best method of ensuring the continuity of their species. Concern with reproduction is, in some of them, so overwhelming that they are adapted to behave both sexually and asexually according to circumstances, in order to make absolutely certain that whatever else happens in the world they will survive. It is as well perhaps that they insist so strongly on the continuity of their species, for if man criminally or clumsily destroys himself and along with him all complex living organisms, it may be that the torch of evolution that was snatched from their tiny cells some 500 million years ago will be thrust back again. Let us examine them: those that preceded us, those whom we may predecease.

The simplest organisms not unnaturally have only one cell. This cell—as with all cells in all living things—is composed of a nucleus embedded in protoplasm around which is a membrane that fences the cell off from the rest of the world. The single-celled organism is free-living, independent, self-sufficient. It is microscopic but it acknowledges no authority outside the boundary of its membrane walls. A cell deprived of its nucleus dies. It feeds by drawing through the membrane whatever nourishment comes its way, and once within the cell the food is slowly digested. It reproduces by binary fission: all the elements in the cell including the nucleus double and the cell then splits in half. The halves share the contents including, of course, the nucleus.[1] Such creatures are then, to all intents and purposes, immortal.

Unicellular organisms are highly successful. They reproduce themselves with consummate ease and, under favourable conditions, with remarkable frequency—half-hourly. Moreover, they have proved their endurance by having survived every vicissitude probably almost unchanged for 1,000 million years. A record of this kind could lay them open to a charge of being ultra-conservative. It is not possible to know whether their lives seem to them to be monotonous. They are far from unimportant. From some or other of them we are certainly derived, and on some of them we are still and will always be dependent.

Bacteria are unicellular organisms. They are so primitive that even the nuclei of their cells are ill defined. They are sometimes classified as plants, and yet there is no cellulose in their cell membranes and with very few exceptions no chlorophyll in their cells. In the soil they effect the decay of plant and animal tissues and so make these available as food for plants. In the rumen of herbivorous animals they break down the hard cellulose membranes of plant cells. Some are capable of assimilating nitrogen and so of building up food from purely inorganic matter. Some cause serious diseases in animals or men—they strive to survive as we do, and they are as indiscriminate and amoral in their choice of food. They are innumerable: a salt-spoonful of rich earth contains hundreds of millions of them.

If there were no bacteria there would be no tuberculosis, no pneumonia and no diphtheria; there would also be no animals and no men.

Apart from bacteria—in spite of the fact that they too are single-celled—are the quite different animal or vegetable flagellata. They are aquatic. Some possess chlorophyll and 'eat' carbon dioxide, others take in food through their cell membranes, and several do both according to the exigencies of their circumstances. Their versatility and their ability to adapt themselves credits them with the possibility of having given rise to multicellular animals and so fathered us all.

With seaweeds or algae we would expect to be on safe plant ground. This is so—nearly. They hover on the brink between land and sea. They are profuse. There are over 18,000 varieties. The single-cell algae are plants pure and simple, except that they are mobile—and feverishly so. There is something else unusual about them: they reproduce in two ways. They do employ conventional cell-division but they are also the forerunners of sex. Special cells released from the parent meet, co-habit, coalesce, become dormant and then resume their normal activities.

Fungi too should be quite clearly vegetable, and they are, usually, despite lacking chlorophyll, but not always. As with the seaweeds there are one-cell varieties. They reproduce by cell-division but they are also capable of feeding like animals, of movement and finally of sexual behaviour. They sort themselves into pairs. They join and spread and migrate from water to land, to dead wood and rotting leaves, always requiring damp, but they are also adapted to withstand drought by forming a protective covering and becoming dormant.

Even ferns have retained characteristics normally associated with animals when circumstances demand, for their sperm like the sperm of moss can swim in water.

On the fringe between the single-celled and multi-celled organisms are the ciliates such as paramecium. This creature has one cell but two nuclei. One of these is concerned with reproduction, which duty it fulfils with masterly perfection. Males and females there are not, but different strains there are. When different strains are in proximity they adhere in pairs and exchange portions of their nuclei through their mouth cavities. This is a type of primitive sexual process involving some reassortment of genetic characters between two individuals. It is an example of an entirely new mechanism for providing the necessary variation underlying evolution.

Leaving behind single-celled organisms we come to the sponges, which are non-mobile animals, and volvox, which is a mobile plant; plants and animals have begun to separate. Sponges are probably derived from the flagellata. Single cells are no longer free-living; social structure and specialization have set in. The individual is beginning to learn to sacrifice his independence to the group. The sponges struck the first blow against unbridled private enterprise, or was it a primitive alga such as the volvox? Volvox is not a colony of individual cells but a single organism with a division of labour among its cells. It has not even yet, however, decided upon the best method of reproduction. It ensures most effectively its continuity by both sexual and asexual reproduction.

At this stage we leave behind the simple organisms and pass on in the next chapter to the explosion of multi-cellular life. It has been thought worthwhile to spend a chapter discussing these very humble organisms because of the light they throw upon the specialized development of all complex living things. They preceded us all. They are living today. They may survive us all. From them even now new plants and animals may be evolving. The experiments they carried out hundreds of millions of years ago provided their successors with the necessary data to enable them to make certain choices. The hovering between sexual and asexual reproduction revealed the advantages and disadvantages of both. The very simplicity of a plant's diet leads to a dead evolutionary end.[2] The complexity of animal diet necessitated the growth of specialized organs and tissues to deal with it. Rooted, plants live or die where they stand. Animals in choosing mobility took the path of danger, adventure and self-reliance. In those far-off days the scenery was being shifted and the stage set for the dual development of fauna and flora. The decision was long being taken, the paths lead far apart.

Finally, when speaking of simple organisms, let it not be forgotten that they are highly complex. Their cells are differentiated into nuclei, cytoplasm and membranes. These are complexes of macromolecules which are all mainly composed of the common elements: hydrogen, oxygen, nitrogen and carbon. All these have fortuitously combined, over ages of unimaginable length, to form a complete individual. An individual which, although lacking brain or limb or any vestige of a nervous system, manages to move, to grow, to mutate, to eat, to react to light and air: to behave, in fact, as though for all the world possessed of the most sublime intelligence.

5 The Explosion of Life

WHEN MAN LETS his mind reflect on such things, he is apt to feel dwarfed by two particular circumstances: the awful isolation and the microscopic proportions of the Planet on which he lives, and the fantastic time scale of evolution against which he must measure the paltry span, not only of his own individual life, but also that of his species.

Man has become acquainted with the smallness of the Earth in comparison with the magnitude of the Universe, and of the brevity of his life in comparison with the longevity of his ancestry, through his attempts to answer two problems: what is happening elsewhere in the Universe, and what are man's origins? Or, to pose the questions differently, is the Earth unique or is it a prototype? Did man evolve from a lower form of life and if so how, when and why?

Inquiry into this second question with all the peripheral problems involved will be pursued throughout the whole of this book. Inquiry into the first question has to be dropped now in this chapter for lack of evidence.

I think that it is generally accepted that we are now reaching the limit of what is discoverable about the Universe by means of observation at a distance and by deductive reasoning;[1] and that this is happening at a time when progress in other branches of science is beginning to enable man to go out into space in order to pursue the search in situ. The twentieth

43

century like the sixteenth is inaugurating an age of discovery. The new worlds of this Earth have been mapped; the new world of the future will be extra-terrestrial.

Before leaving the problems of these new worlds to be solved by the astronauts, there is just one point left to be made by us, the observers at a distance. The processes described in the last chapter, which led inanimate matter through a number of intermediate stages to acquire and display finally and fully all the characteristics of living things, are processes which seem to have been duplicated or matched beyond the confines of this Earth. We believe this to be so because our proximity to Mars enables us to observe what appears to be the spread during the Martian spring of green vegetation from the equator towards the poles, accompanied by the retreat of the circumpolar snow lines.

Whether there is animal and human, as well as plant life on Mars we do not yet know, although it seems extremely unlikely. Neither do we know whether—if there is none—it might one day, if left to its own devices, yield higher forms, nor whether it may once have yielded higher forms which have become extinct; whether, in fact, it is ascending or descending the scale of evolution. A thin atmosphere and a deficiency of moisture indicate, without proving, that with plant life Mars may have exploited its resources and environment to the limit; or else that the planet is in decline: a cemetery of higher forms of life from which eventually even vegetation will disappear. Loss of atmosphere is fatal and irreversible.

There is no intention of going into the matter here. Speculation is intensely interesting but inevitably inconclusive; besides it seems pointless to pursue an argument with scanty evidence when by waiting it will be resolved by first-hand account. The matter has been brought up here because of the outstanding importance of the discovery — if it is confirmed — that another planet has independently given birth to plant life. On a cosmic scale it is true to say that this knowledge will be so significant that further discoveries made by direct observation are bound to be — if not to seem — trivial by comparison. For it will prove that the Earth is neither a fluke, a unique, unpredictable and unrepeatable anomaly in a lifeless Universe, nor the unique creation of the mind of a creator.

This knowledge will prove that the immensely complicated processes which lead to the building up and growth of plant cells — the amino-acids and proteins, the protoplasm and nucleus, the photosynthesis and chlorophyll — are common, universal phenomena: the inevitable destiny of inorganic matter in association in an appropriate environment. Life 'happens' under favourable conditions everywhere. There must be a cosmic 'drive' towards association, complexity, growth, differentiation and reproduction. The biologist, as well as the physicist, is handling not merely terrestrial but universal concepts.

Soon we shall know a great deal more. Now, however, it is necessary to return to the study of the Earth and the millions of years that intervened between the protozoa of the previous chapter and the advent of man. It is as well to do so, however, in the awareness that our study is, without almost any doubt at all, being paralleled on countless millions of other planets.

As has already been said, fossil records begin with the opening of the Cambrian Period rather more than 500 million years ago. It is on fossil records that we are mainly dependent as we pick our way through these immensities of time until the present day. Verging on the miraculous though it seems, that so deeply embedded a record has been unearthed at all, it is as well to remind oneself that although fossils yield information that is exact, there are limits to the kind and quality of that information. It is necessary to be precise about this because the outline of animal and plant evolution that follows is inevitably biased in the direction of the sources of available information. To be specific: a fossil reveals obviously first and foremost the bone structure of an animal; also its size and weight, the presence or absence of brain and nervous system, and its method of reproduction. Even its means of locomotion and chosen habitat can be deduced; so can its diet from an analysis of its intestines; so can the climate of the period, by relating its diet to the location of its discovery. The brilliance and energy and patience with which all this evidence has been brought together and correlated is almost beyond belief. There is, however, at least one aspect of animal life which fossils fail almost entirely to reveal to us: their social life. Fossils reveal the size of the brain, but not what went on inside it.[2] They reveal the presence or absence and location of a nervous system, but they can tell us nothing about its sensitivity. Fossils tell us when and where and even sometimes how animals lived and died, but they cannot tell us about their family and group life: their patterns of behaviour, their moods and their rituals. For our knowledge of such things we are driven to rely upon their survivors which are our contemporaries. The difficulties of observation are immense. The study of them is of recent origin since their existence and importance is just being realized. It is not surprising; human psychology and sociology are new sciences too — recent and only recently respectable.

With the limitations of palaeontology in mind we proceed now to an outline of the volumes it has discovered. Fossil records trace with great accuracy the evolution of species through the last 500 million years. Tantalizingly, however, rock records scarcely exist prior to that period, and for that reason it has not so far been possible to find fossils of the prototypes from which all the main divisions of animal life are derived. Pre-Cambrian rocks are so distorted that although some fossils have been described they do not invalidate the above statement.

Our knowledge of organisms prior to that date is therefore mainly based upon reconstructions derived, on the one hand, from embryology and comparative anatomy and, on the other, from a study of the recapitulation by embryos in contemporary species of the evolutionary history through which they have passed. This latter point will be discussed in greater detail later.

The rocks of the Cambrian Period are rich in fossils, all of which, without any exceptions, are invertebrate. A further 200 million years had to pass before the backbone was 'invented'. Life was not only spineless, it was also entirely marine.[3] Only the seas had been colonized, and they were inhabited by animals possessing shells or some solid structure which was preservable. Their survivors play a humble role now on the Planet they once dominated.

No plant and no living creature grew or moved over the utterly naked, sand-blown, rock-strewn earth. Yet every division of all living things—bird, fish and animal—was already represented in the sea except, of course, the vertebrates.

The simplest fossil remains are of creatures which differ from their soft-bodied ancestors solely by the addition of protective shells or external skeletons. They too begin life as blobs of protoplasm, but instead of remaining in this form they undergo a process of development which involves the secretion either of calcium carbonate or of silica. These secretions are extracted from sea water and woven into shell coverings or spiny projections varying widely in pattern and texture.

Whether these organisms went to the lengths of encasing themselves in protective shells and of arming themselves with noxious projections with anything resembling intent, or whether the secretion of calcium or silica is an involuntary chemical process giving its fortunate possessor a temporary advantage, are matters of supreme interest and complexity, but they must be outside the argument of this book. For the moment we are concerned purely with a reconstruction of the past; an inquiry into *what* happened, not why or how—infinitely more difficult, more controversial, more speculative problems.

The most numerous, widespread and successful invertebrates of the Cambrian Period were the trilobites of which there are no survivors. They specialized in the secretion of a thick shell, which by defending them against attack gave them temporary ascendancy. But the way of evolution does not lie in the ability to wrap oneself up ponderously in hard casing and so obtain immunity from the hazards of one's environment, but in mobility, agility and versatility.

However, the invertebrates had made great advances. They pioneered a complex division of cellular labour; they could boast of digestive, reproductive and nervous systems. They grew eyes and limbs. They had their day. They had for long been menaced on all sides by the vertebrates who owe them so much. They are represented today by such august creatures as the octopus and the giant squid who failed to sense the wind of change.

By the beginning of the Devonian Period, some 300 million years ago, the rocks reveal the rising star of vertebracy; animals with backbones were on the way towards establishing a supremacy which they achieved, and have not yet relinquished—and never, it seems, will. In those far-off days the possession of a backbone became a passport to fame. It is as though some distant, antique nonconformist trilobite had revolted against the Establishment—hoary to the tune of 200 million years—and reversed his anatomy. The rigid outer shell encasing a soft body became a soft body encasing a hard, but more or less jointed internal skeleton, hinged or centred on a spinal cord. The development, of course, was gradual. A rudimentary spine with a cartilaginous rod running its entire length is found in a survivor from those days: the lancelet, which has no fins, no limbs, no eyes, no ears, no markedly differentiated brain. It was, however, despite these undeniable disadvantages, on or close to the main line of evolutionary development.

All life was still confined to the water. It was the Age of Fishes. They reached the zenith of their power and ascendancy. The sea will never again be the chosen environment of the great.

It is not possible to say with absolute certainty what occurred finally to initiate the colonization of the land, although it is easy to understand why the sea was the cradle of life. The shift from sea to land began to take place towards the end of the Devonian Period. It is known to have been a period of great aridity. This must have led to the drying up or conversion into swamps of some or all of the inland seas which simultaneously became land-locked. Fish trapped in these declining seas with no means of escape were faced with the alternative of death or of finding a means of breathing on land—that is to say taking in oxygen directly from the air—during those increasingly frequent and lengthening times of the year when their lakes dried up. Whatever form it was that the challenge took, it was met. A class of vertebrate, Choanichthynes, in addition to possessing gill-slits—by means of which fishes normally extract oxygen from sea water——had lungs. Their direct descendants are still with us; they inhabit swamps and switch over to lung-breathing for the seasonal drought. Lungs, the ability to breathe on land, and paired fins (which endowed their owners with rudimentary 'legs') enabled them to make the first awkward ponderous movements over an entirely new world: the dry land. The vast and portentous shift from sea to shore had begun. Some pioneers made the change and then thought better of it. They returned to the sea; they are still there.

The colonization of the land by animals had to be preceded by its colonization by plants. For on the land as in the sea, although animals nourish themselves by feeding on each other, finally somewhere down the scale, but certainly at the bottom of it, there must be vegetarians. Carnivorousness is all very well but it is not self-supporting. Plant life was therefore necessarily in the vanguard of the invasion. Evolution, like an army, marches with an eye cocked in the direction of its stomach.

Some varieties of seaweeds were becoming habituated to a semi-aquatic life on the fringes of the oceans and on tidal estuaries. However, all these plants are primitive to the extent that structurally they are not differentiated into root and trunk, stem, leaf and branch. When this division of labour was achieved, the land—or that part of it which was covered by layers of sedimentary soil—became congenial to growth. Plants could draw water out of the soil by means of elaborate root systems—horsetails, ferns and tree-ferns—although without flowers and with scales for leaves. The spread of vegetation was accelerated by the development of reproduction by seed in place of spore. This modification in plants is analogous to a similar development which took place later among the reptiles. A seed, unlike a spore, is an embryo fitted to fend for itself by the provision of food within a protective coat.

Not unnaturally the first settlers on the land were amphibious; animals which were reluctant to commit themselves irreparably to either element. The amphibians are ancestral to all land vertebrates, but they are now represented by but few effete survivors—the salamander, the frog, the newt and the toad—which give small indication of the noble and pioneering role played by their stock some 300 million years ago. They still pay tribute to the time-honoured traditions of that antique past for, although they can live equally well on the land as in the water, to the water they must return to breed and lay their eggs. They begin life as tadpoles, still inevitably in infancy confined to the element in which all life originated.

During the next 50 million years life exploded and spread in prodigious variety over the entire surface of the globe. Vast and primitive forests, favoured by a tropical climate, prevailed from pole to pole; grew up and stretched far, wide and high, finally to lay down those coal deposits from which the Carboniferous Period derives its name.

With the termination of this long summer, the easy and simple ways of life that its warm and even temperatures had protected came to an end. The climate became colder and drier. Great changes took place over the surface of the Earth. Mountain ranges were thrown up, old land masses were inundated and new ones created. In this cataclysm the weak were eliminated. The strong and the adaptable survived. It is at this time that the rocks tell of the rise to absolute supremacy of a new race: the reptiles. They dominated the Earth for 150 million years: until 70 million years ago. It is a period which is astounding in its length as well as in the prodigious size and variety of the animals that lived in it. Success in the long run is apt to lead to failure. Complacency is the result of the absence of a challenge. The reptiles, whose enormous images are sufficient to strike terror into the stoutest heart, which weighed up to forty tons and had a spread of thirty yards and even whose names – brontosaurus, triceratops and tyrannosaurus rex – are hardly reassuring, were often quite harmless vegetarians. They concentrated on brawn instead of brain. They would not inherit the Earth. Their bulky and exotic rule came to an end; they shared a similar fate to the amphibians. They are represented now by comparatively few and mainly humble offspring: lizards, snakes, crocodiles, turtles and tortoises. The success of the reptiles lay rooted in the beginning of their long career, before they began to concentrate on sheer bulk. They achieved a notable step in the direction of greater care of their young. Their eggs were so constituted as to provide food for the embryo on hatching. There was also no longer any need for them to return to the water to breed. So long did it take evolution to work such seemingly minor and insignificant changes.

The decline and fall of species is still in the nature of an enigma. This does not mean that no explanation can be offered, but that the explanations offered are either not entirely convincing or not completely verified. Catastrophic changes of geography and climate do not seem to be adequate explanations in themselves, although it is easy to underestimate their importance. Throughout this chapter we have been speaking in terms of tens of millions of years. It is easier to speak of them than to imagine them. The recorded history of man, stretched to its utmost, extends over a period of 7,000 years; and the visualization of even that requires a strong effort of the imagination.

The rise and fall of species although often referred to as 'sudden' were, however, by historical standards excessively leisurely. The changes that occurred in the climate of the

Earth were almost certainly extremely gradual; they would, however, be just as lethal in the long run, except that they would give time for the few more active, less cumbersome forms of life to migrate. But the *will* to migrate would depend upon an animal having the intelligence or instinct to do so. The *ability* to migrate would depend upon an animal's environment—hemmed in by mountains or deserts; confined to an island. The enumeration of the difficulties could be continued almost indefinitely, and when to all these are added the innate conservatism of individual animals and their ingrained sense of 'territory', it is conceivable that even the most slow and creeping changes from tropical to temperate and temperate to arctic conditions might have initiated no reaction, no migration, no attempt at self-preservation and thus have proved fatal. The very slowness of climatic change might even contribute to its ultimately fatal effect. For in this way no variation would be noticed from generation to generation. The species concerned would simply become gradually less prolific and finally extinct, not with a bang but with a whimper.

Climate changes gradually;[4] geography does not. Again we have to tax our imagination to the utmost in order to try to understand what it would be like to live during a period of mountain building when, for instance, ranges as high and extensive as the Himalayas were lifted sheer out of the bottom of the ocean and thrust 30,000 feet into the sky. The familiar outline of the Earth that we know from our atlases is modern by geological standards.

Mountains, lakes, rivers, valleys, seas, coasts and continents have shifted, been obliterated, lifted up, eroded, created and recreated—repeatedly—and will continue to be so. Survival would be difficult even for man in such circumstances; how much more difficult must it have been for animals caught in such cataclysms? 'Mother Earth' has crushed and drowned a goodly proportion of her progeny.

So much for climate and geography. To return to the reptiles whose disappearance we are trying to account for; they were not only subjected to the dangers and dilemmas referred to in the last paragraph, they were also probably outwitted— not, of course, overpowered— by a new group, the mammals, who fed partly on reptile eggs. One other 'explanation' has been advanced: races may die of exhaustion; cells may tire and lose their vitality. If racial fatigue does in fact occur, the reptiles were ripe for it. Their dynasty had ruled the Earth for 150 million years.

It may well be that all these processes were at work. One is inclined to seek for a single explanation for a phenomenon which has complex and interlocking causes. A change of climate certainly occurred about 70 million years ago. It was accompanied by a general raising of the continental massifs. If these environmental catastrophes— which in themselves may have proved fatal to the larger reptiles, inert and brooding in their chilling swamps— were accompanied by the depredations of the mammals and a general cytological decline, the combination may be enough to account for the fall of the reptile kingdom.

With the beginning of the Cenozoic Period, 70 million years ago, we move into modern times and pass to a study of the animal life with which all of us are at least vaguely familiar. Since man is a mammal and since the rest of this book is concerned almost exclusively with an analysis of him, time will be well spent in discussing his distant ancestors and his remote cousins.

The prodigious variety of reptilian life during the preceding Mesozoic Period had the effect of obscuring all other species. Mammals did not suddenly 'arrive'. There had been mammals in the world for 200 million years already when the reptilian supremacy came to an end. The destruction of the reptiles created a vacuum. It was this vacuum that the mammals filled, whether it was partly of their own making or not.

Mammals were not very numerous, not very large, not very aggressive. They were widespread and unspecialized. The remains of the most primitive have been found in every continent except Australia. They differ from other animals mainly in two ways: in the care of their young and in the size of their brains. By definition, of course, a mammal is an animal that gives milk to its young: a characteristic which does not at first glance appear vastly significant. But quite apart from the nutritional value of the milk, which is indisputable, there are important side-effects. The provision of milk involves post-natal care. It is possible to conclude that the young benefited less from the milk than from the presence of one or both parents which the provision of milk necessitated. For in this way family life, and so a new kind of social life, began. Offspring became dependent upon the adult members of their own species. A completely new pattern of behaviour was set in motion.

It is realized that the value of a survey as abbreviated as the one given in this chapter is open to question. Condensation of matter may lead to so many omissions that the picture is distorted beyond recognition. The reader will decide for himself. I have thought it necessary to include this chapter because of the chronological bridge it provides between matter and man; because of the evolutionary lessons contained in it, and finally, because man is so recent a development by the evolutionary clock yet so old in his own estimation, that he should be made aware of his sources. If man would regard himself simply as a highly evolved animal he might begin to understand himself better, and take a more realistic view of his shortcomings, instead of trying sickeningly and unsuccessfully to cover them up.

The results achieved during the 500 million years covered by this chapter seem minuscule in proportion to the time involved. The fact seems to be that evolution is dependent upon some sort of social life before it can accelerate.

The animals which superseded each other gained their successively and excessively long ascendancy in every case for very good reasons. But each in turn rested on its laurels, became large, elaborate and specialized. The crustacea encased themselves in shells and relied upon defence. The fish were content to remain in an element which is ideal as a womb or a nursery, but which is so dense and so dominant that its occupants are mastered by the restrictions it imposes on them. The reptiles concentrated on bulk and an elaboration of forms and neglected their brains. The birds sacrificed everything to supreme lightness of structure.

Success depended always and will go on depending upon offence rather than defence, on agility rather than bulk, on brain rather than brawn.

When social evolution was superimposed on organic evolution, the family, the group, the herd, the flock became new evolutionary units which were no longer concerned uniquely with the duty of preserving their species but also with its development.

For how long social evolution has been functioning it is extremely difficult to say. Even in its most primitive form it possesses a group memory, a group experience and leadership of a kind. A division of labour begins to take place among the members of the group, which is analogous to the division of labour that took place long before among the cells in the individual. It has for long been common knowledge that the social life of insects is highly organized; but, as a general rule, man has always regarded himself as the pioneer in this field. Yet the nuptial flight of dragonflies, the nesting arrangements of wasps and the dance of the bees are but a few examples of immensely complex methods of communication and patterns of behaviour.

The social life of animals has only recently attracted the attention it undoubtedly deserves. It is probably still evolving. It simply must not be compared with the reckless speed of our own. Comparison between its development and ours can, however, be highly instructive as with the most universal sense of territory, to take but one example. In the water, in the air and on the land, fish, birds and animals are nearly always insistent upon marking out frontiers for themselves which, however otherwise pacific they are, they will defend to the death. Evidence of man's identical behaviour is not, unfortunately, lacking.

6 The Unit of Life

The hen is the egg's way of making another egg.

Samuel Butler, *Life and Habit*

CELLS HAVE BEEN mentioned not infrequently during the course of the last three chapters of this book—cells in isolation, cells in multiplication and cells in division. So far their importance has been implicit. The time has come to analyse them and try to draw their secret out of them. It would be unrealistic to approach a study of man and mind without first of all exploring what there is to be known, not only about man's ancestry, but also about the content of that ancestry and so the ways and means of inheritance .

The cell is to biology what the atom is to physics—its unit. The atom and the cell are stable, independent, self-sufficient and microscopic. They are the bricks with which the inanimate and animate aspects of nature have been constructed. Where these two aspects overlap there is a complexity of atomic, and a simplicity of cellular structures cementing two apparently opposite poles together.

The parallel roles played by the atom and the cell have naturally enough led to a correspondingly intensive research into the structure of each. The atomic physicist has run a longer and an apparently more spectacular course. The cytologist was a late starter; his success has been immense but less spectacular—so far—not because his findings have been more difficult to understand, but because they have not led to, nor do they seem to threaten to have, any wild and terrible and tragic sequels.

58

But to turn from the general to the particular and to begin at the beginning.

All living things are composed entirely of one or more cells. Cells do not vary in size according to whether they are the constituents of an elephant or the constituents of a mouse. They vary in size according only to their functions. They vary in number according to the size of the organism they form. They are as various as the rodent population of Hamelin; there are liver cells, sex cells, brain cells, muscle cells, nerve cells, etc. Some idea of the number of cells that are present in the human body, for example, may be gathered from the fact that a cubic centimetre of liver tissue contains about 200 million. But the purpose of this chapter is not to add them up, but to break them down.

Every cell is composed of two parts: the nucleus in the centre surrounded by a fine membrane wall, and the cytoplasm that surrounds the nucleus and is, in its turn, enclosed by a membrane which holds the cell intact. Briefly each cell has, therefore, a nucleus, a nuclear membrane, a circumnuclear cytoplasm and finally an outer cell wall. The nucleus is like a citadel in a small, tightly defended town.

Food, filtered into the cell through the outer cell wall, passes into the semi-fluid cytoplasm where specialized bodies digest it or synthesize it, and thus make it available for cell growth. The cytoplasm with its membrane can therefore be regarded as the body of the cell which performs, under normal healthy conditions, the business of providing itself and the nucleus with suitable nourishment. There are certainly surprises in store for us here, however, for the cytoplasm is far from being a flabby undifferentiated jelly; it contains several highly complex organelles whose functions are beginning to be understood. Moreover, the type of proteins that it should manufacture are communicated to it by chemical messengers from the nucleus. It is therefore a work-shop as well as a digestive system.

Pressing on deep into the interior of the cell, we cross the second frontier and reach the nucleus. This is the heart of the matter; the Holy of Holies, the source, the cradle, the womb and the essence. It the life and we the living are face to face. Whatever other duties the nucleus may perform—and they are certainly many—it performs the not inconsiderable function of ensuring the continuation of coherent life and of regulating the form that that life shall take.

As with the nucleus of the atom, so with the nucleus of the cell; the search does not end there. It begins again on a deeper level. The indivisible is always being divided.

Inside the nucleus of every cell, of every plant and animal are found a fixed number, according to species, of thread-like bodies called chromosomes, and throughout the length of all chromosomes, in single file, lie the genes. They are the func-tional units of heredity. Chromosomes vary in shape and length. They exist in pairs.[1] The number of pairs per nucleus depends upon the species and varies from one to over fifty—man has twenty-three pairs, except in abnormal cases.

Just before a cell divides, every chromosome in the nucleus doubles so that each of the daughter-cells carries away with it a full—normal for the species—complement of chromosomes, and consequently of genes. The process of cell division is known as mitosis. Mitosis is the common method by which a cell divides. Sex cells follow a different procedure; they will be discussed later in this chapter.

It will thus be seen that death, as we know it, does not exist in the cellular world except in rare cases of accident, for the division of one cell into two is the result of growth not of degeneration. There has therefore been no break in the con-tinuity of life. It is an endless stream flowing towards an unknown future, and back; back to the beginning of time, to the first cell that divided and beyond to the first neutron – or whatever.

Cell division is a highly efficient, one might say an absolutely foolproof way of ensuring the survival of an organism. We have already discussed in this book some single-celled organisms that have been doing just precisely this for some 1,000 million years, which seems cast iron evidence enough. But when one has paid tribute to the longevity of this method, one has paid all the tribute that is thinkable to pay. For though single-celled organisms have solved the problem of survival, they have certainly never broached, let alone solved, any other. The reason is not far to seek; there is no scope for development when repetition is the rage. There is no change of diet. They digest their food and grow; a certain size having been attained the surface of the outer cell wall becomes disproportionate to the appetite of the body. The body divides and so becomes proportionate again. Nothing new is ever introduced or entertained for evolution to get its teeth into. The parent cell divides the inheritance exactly in half and in their turn the beneficiaries will do the same, and so on, and so on.

It was not until sex was invented that the wheels of evolution really began to hum. Sex introduced novelty by the joining together of two dissimilar sets of chromosomes; it also introduced death on a vast scale by building up an adult organism solely for the purpose of producing sex-cells. This purpose achieved, so far as the sex-cells were concerned, the body could die – and the body, of course, does die. It is quite a price to pay, but there is nothing to be done about it now. The course was irrevocably decided a very, very long time ago. Evolution does not retrace its steps, so sex has to be suffered and enjoyed.

But to return to the nucleus; it is time to consider how sex works and what sex has to work on and with.

Ordinary cell division, known as mitosis, which is the normal method by which most cells, other than sex cells, divide,[2] involves as we have seen a simple cleavage of the nucleus along with the rest of the cell. For this to happen a doubling of its contents of chromosomes and genes must obviously take place before division, in order to ensure that the daughter-cells inherit exactly the same complement of chromosomes and genes as the parent cell. This means that every potentiality of the original is passed on to the offspring. (The fertilized egg has, for example, none of the specialized characters of the hen — a hen cannot be foretold by the study of the egg. Yet the egg will specialize the hen out of itself by a controlled release of its potentialities.)

The asexual reproduction practised by single-celled organisms, and by the body cells in higher organisms, is reproduction by fission. Sexual reproduction is the opposite: it is reproduction by fusion. Now reproduction of this kind possesses enormous evolutionary advantages — which will be discussed later — but it has also an enormous technical difficulty to overcome. The technical difficulty clearly is this: unless some mechanism exists to prevent it, every time the sex-cells fused, the contents of the nucleus would fuse also, with the result that each generation would find itself saddled with twice the number of chromosomes and genes possessed by its predecessor. Such a progression had to be overcome. Disaster is avoided by the functioning of a mechanism which ensures that sex-cells are always produced with only half the normal complement of chromosomes. Consequently sex-cells instead of having pairs have single chromosomes so that when they are mated, the resultant fused cell, the zygote, is 'normal'; that is to say, it has pairs of chromosomes again —

one from the male, one from the female, and so the life cycle goes on.

In order to understand the effects of sexual reproduction and why evolution has favoured this method, it is necessary to retrace our steps a little and take a longer and closer look at the chromosome-gene complex.

Before any cell divides, all its chromosomes are observed to shorten and thicken which is due to coiling. Genes are strung close together along the entire length of the chromosome. They can be imagined as minute beads threaded tightly on a fine fibre. On this they coil slowly like a spring that is being gently wound up. All the chromosomes are passing through this same phase together just prior to division. However many chromosomes there are, there will, of course, be the same number in all the cells of the individual organism and, indeed, in all the cells of all the organisms of that particular species. Chromosomes are visible only under a high-powered microscope, yet each will contain anything from several hundred to several thousand genes.

Now since chromosomes become paired again as the result of the fusion of a male set with a female set, all genes become paired again, too. They have 'opposite numbers', so that each gene has a corresponding gene with a similar function.

At the outset, for ease of explanation, it is best perhaps to consider each gene as performing a particular task, or ensuring a specific function for which, in company with its 'opposite number', it is uniquely responsible. To take a simple example: a pair of genes are responsible for eye colour. The genes may concur or conflict. When they conflict, one or other is preferred, and is called dominant; the other is deferred and is said to be recessive. This, in practice, means that if both genes are for brown, the result will be brown;

that if one is blue and the other brown, and brown is dominant, then brown the eyes will be, and there will be nothing in that generation to show that beneath the appearance of brown there lies a recessive blue. This recessive gene for blue eyes is latent and is, of course, capable of asserting itself in a future generation when it meets another recessive gene of its own kind.

That is of course true. But it is true only up to a point, for the situation is infinitely more complicated.

Genes are not in fact isolated particles of heredity strung along a thread. They are in contact: in physical contact, and in communication. So that although a particular gene is primarily concerned with some specific task, it is nevertheless jointly concerned with the proper co-ordination of its task with those of its neighbours.

Eye colour was taken because it is a simple example, but it is not representative of the complexity of the manifold roles which genes are called upon to play. Every part of the body has cells which are differentiated to perform special functions. The genes co-ordinate these functions and upon their qualities depends largely the quality of that part of the body for which they are responsible. This specialization of cells is so endemic that cells removed from the organism of which they are part die since they are unable to take up an independent existence. So far in this chapter an attempt has been made to create a picture of the cell; to enumerate its contents, to explain the functions of its parts and to explain what occurs when division takes place. This knowledge in brief outline is necessary in order to understand how and why evolution takes place and what the laws of inheritance are, so far as we know them.

All discussion of living things in this book has so far been conducted on a descriptive level, enumerating the steps that have led over 1,000 million years from life emerging from matter until the age of the mammals. All those living things, plant and animal, during all that time were composed of one or more cells containing nuclei, containing chromosomes and genes. It is, however, only during this century that the mechanism of the genes has been discovered,[3] thus enabling us to become acquainted with the raw material of evolution, and to fill in some of the gaps that Darwin was well aware existed in his evolutionary synthesis.

These preliminaries over, it is now possible to approach the problem of what is going on inside the cell, and more particularly the cell nucleus, to enable evolutionary changes to occur in living organisms.

Physical evolution takes place because certain changes, called mutations, occur in the genes, and because certain recombinations take place among the genes in the sex-cells. These mutations and recombinations are reproduced in the offspring; certain of them become dominant and certain of them become recessive. In any case, as a result of this, offspring occur which are 'new'. They may be better or less well adapted. Those that are better adapted are at an advantage and are therefore more likely to survive, and therefore more likely to have offspring and propagate themselves than those that are at a disadvantage. The fittest, in fact, survive. Nature is extravagant in her production of progeny. This extravagance—this excessive over-production—is designed to ensure the survival of a species at the cost of the destruction of a vast surplus. A struggle, a competition inevitably ensues. This struggle to survive is a tenet of Darwinism: its implications and meaning will be discussed in the next chapter. Here we are concerned with the raw material: the genes, their mutations and recombinations and the mechanisms that favour or expel them.

All parts of the body grow as a result of simple cell division. A cell divides and becomes two, the two divide and become four and so on. Thus all the specialized cells of body, brain and nerve increase in number and bring about the growth of the whole organism. When the organism dies, all these cells, of course, die with it. Nothing of all that is therefore, so far as we know, directly inherited.

The responsibility for inheritance devolves upon the sex-cells, of which only a few of the millions produced will in fact carry out the function of fertilization for which they are intended. Consequently it is the gene constitution of the sex-cells which is studied for an understanding of the mechanism of inheritance and of the processes of evolution.

A man has forty-six chromosomes in every one of his body cells, and every chromosome is believed to contain several thousand genes, which gives some idea of the astronomical number of possible combinations. Each pair of chromosomes is derived from the joining together of one male and one female chromosome in that one fertilized egg-cell from which the whole man has originated.

Now that we know a great deal about what occurs when the sex-cells are produced, we are able to see how these possibilities are created.

Firstly, all the chromosomes in the nucleus sort themselves out into pairs and lie close together. Every chromosome divides and the members of each pair move apart, except where they are held together by breakage and rejoining which causes a crossing-over. Division now sorts the resulting chromosomes out into four cells. The crossing-over has created new combinations of genes. Crossing-over does not always occur, but it is much more usual than the simple doubling of the pairs without breakage and rejoining.

The fact of crossing-over enables us to form a more subtle

picture of the gene than the rather coarse image of beads on a thread. Genes are discrete units of heredity. They do not grade into each other, but they should be looked upon as sections of the chromosome existing between two points of possible breakage.

This crossing-over process, combined with the new combinations of chromosomes inherent in sexual reproduction, gives opportunities of immense variation *within the existing gene complex*. But if this were all that evolution had to work on, admittedly there would be infinite variation, but only variation on a theme. The theme would be restricted by the character of a fixed gene structure.

The raw material of evolution is of two kinds, with rather rare and unimportant exceptions. Firstly, there are gene-mutations and, secondly, changes of position of one or more genes within the chromosome.

It is necessary to elaborate. The genes are isolated from each other only in a physical sense, which does not prevent them from being interdependent and intercommunicating, and interacting with their more immediate neighbours. They are like actors who are primarily concerned with their own parts, but who are dependent upon all the other members of the cast to give meaning and substance to their roles. This means that when a mutation occurs it is usually a change for the worse, for the gene structure is necessarily delicately balanced, and if one of its members changes it is more likely that the balance will be upset than improved. To pursue the same metaphor—if one of the actors chooses to effect a change in his part, the likelihood is that it will upset the rest of the cast and that it will be rare for such a change to be beneficial. If it is beneficial then the change will be incorporated in all future productions, and it is precisely this that happens when a mutation is advantageous. In any case when a mutation occurs, unless it is lethal, it will be incorporated into the constitution of the cell until and unless another occurs to change it again, or change it back again. When a gene mutates it is not issuing, as it were, an ultimatum to the cell, it is making a proposal which is subject to negotiation. If the mutation is not lethal or sterilizing, it will continue to exist and its neighbours will modify themselves to contain it. In any case the gene has an 'opposite number' in its paired chromosome. The mutant gene will in all probability be dominated by its established partner and become recessive; available finally perhaps to assert itself if a situation or change of environment calls for it.

The fact that chromosomes are paired enables an infinite number of variations to lie concealed and stored to be drawn upon when occasion demands. It should be realized that any species may be faced with changing conditions of a sudden and catastrophic kind, or presented with pressing and unexpected possibilities of expansion. If the gene structure were not plastic adaptation would be too slow to enable a species to face a disaster or profit from an opportunity. The existence of recessive genes enables a species to hold in reserve a vast stock of adaptations which can quickly be called into play if need be.

How a recessive gene becomes dominant is yet to be expounded. It is however hinted that in some way the gene is modified by its environment, that is to say, by the total gene complex. Its value becomes 'recognized'.

It is clear, then, at least that evolution does not occur through a series of sharp steps. Evolution feels its way forward with the utmost circumspection. It tests the ground before it treads on it. It permits the most revolutionary newcomer to make a proposal, but it never adopts a proposal without subjecting it to the most virulent cross-examination and the severest criticism. It acts, in fact, as man should act— with complete freedom and nonconformity of mind. No change is too spectacular to contemplate, yet no change without the most rigorous tests will be adopted.

And yet the processes of change at work within the gene complex appear to be random. The geneticist has discovered nothing that could possibly lead us to believe that gene-mutations and changes of position are wilfully brought about by the organisms they inhabit. The genes lying in their ultra-microscopic thousands along their chromosomes are like so many monstrously large packs of cards. These packs are constantly being shuffled and cut, and to make confusion worse confounded, individual cards are from time to time and at random changing their symbols. All this is happening without apparently any sort of guidance from the organism they inhabit. It would seem to be chaotic. Yet the genes are subject to a rigid control, exercised by the environment of the cell in which they live, and of the organism of which that cell forms a part. It is in fact under the control of the whole circumstances of its existence. Life is struggling to evolve— not, be it noted, struggling to survive for it won that victory long ago, as the last 1,000 million years reveal. It is struggling to achieve something which can be called progress or complexity of mind. And that struggle is fought on a single front. The environment selects the gene constitution that is fittest to survive. How this conclusion is reached and its import and meaning are discussed more fully in the next chapter.

7 Variation, Selection and Inheritance

THE FURORE RAISED by the publication, a little more than a century ago, of Darwin's *Origin of Species* was due largely to the fact that the theory of evolution that it advanced contradicted the account of the Creation as narrated in Chapters I and II of the Book of Genesis.

It is perhaps necessary to recall that until 1859 the Book of Genesis was regarded as a divinely inspired scientific treatise which, despite its totally primitive and anthropomorphic approach, had explained once and for all time the origin of the Universe and everything it contained. It was popularly believed that God by creative fiat had brought into existence in 4004 B.C.[1] every living thing that moved over the face of the Earth, that crawled on its beaches or swam in its seas. This was the theory of Special Creation. Each species had been created and had remained unchanged, appearing brand new out of the divine crucible some 6,000 years ago—the rhinoceros and the poppy; the begonia, the bumble-bee and the bear. Man, of course, was separate. The whole world of nature existed simply to please or nourish him. The animals were 'back-stairs'; there was no hint of a relationship.

Darwin and Wallace were not the first evolutionists, but they were the first to produce both a devastating weight of evidence in support of the mutability of species and to put forward a convincing theory to account for it.

70

But before discussing the theory of evolution that they advanced, the modifications and additions that have since been made to it, and the problems that still remain to be solved, it seems an appropriate moment to make a brief survey of the arguments upon which all theories of the evolution—as opposed to the Special Creation—of living things are founded.

Firstly, there is the evidence provided by fossils. Layer upon layer of sedimentary rock, stacked like cards in a pack, provide us with a continuous fossil record which leads us back over more than 500 million years of the Earth's history. A study of those strata which have most recently been laid down reveals that they contain fossils of familiar animals and plants. Moreover, as we proceed through the successive layers and thus the farther we move away in time from the present, the less familiar the fossils become; they may be related to existing forms or they may be extinct species. It is consequently possible to trace through millions of years the evolution of species, and to reconstruct a picture of the animal and plant world at every epoch in the story of life. Where records are particularly good, it is possible to recapitulate all the intermediate stages through which species have passed; to know, for example, that horses at one time were no larger than dogs, and that the pig and the camel, like the bird and the snake, have a common ancestor.

Secondly, there is the evidence provided by comparative anatomy. The pedigrees of both extinct and living forms are traced by this means. Relationships between species are shown beyond any possibility of doubt. If, for example, man's kinship with the anthropoid apes were doubted by anyone not content to accept their striking resemblance as evidence, it is only necessary to appeal to the anatomist who can demonstrate that every bone we possess can be paralleled by a corresponding bone in the skeletons of the great apes. Add to this the identical structures and patterns of muscle, the identical systems of blood circulation, the specialization of the fore-limbs for handling, the comparable size and the similarity in the organization of the brain. The resemblances are almost too numerous to catalogue.

Thirdly, there is the evidence provided by embryology. Animals that as adults are almost totally dissimilar often bear striking resemblances to each other as embryos. Tortoises, lizards, birds and snakes, for example, are difficult to tell apart in the embryonic stage. The embryos can often be dis-tinguished only by their size. Resemblances of this kind, indicating an undoubted relationship, may be prolonged into infancy, as, for example, in the similarity of immature plumage in birds. The human embryo is, of course, no exception. It recapitulates in nine months the embryonic history of the species. At different stages it possesses the gill-slits of an embryonic fish; the extra-embryonic membrane of an embryonic reptile; the hairiness of an embryonic ape, and so on and so on.

Fourthly, there is the evidence provided by the systematists. No matter what set of rules is applied to the classification of plants and animals into species, sub-species, varieties, families, etc., it is impossible to draw clear lines of demarcation be-tween them. On the fringes of all groups are types which defy definite classification. They blend into each other by a series of almost insensible gradations, which is exactly the reverse of what would be the case if species had been specially created.

Fifthly, there is the evidence provided by the existence of vestigial organs, that is to say, organs which are disappearing due to their no longer performing a useful function; such as the wings of flightless birds, or the appendix in a man. On a theory of Special Creation vestigial organs are utterly meaningless, while the view that plants and animals have evolved, acquiring new functions and losing old ones, renders them immediately intelligible.

These are the main arguments in support of the evolution of species, which were documented and developed exhaustively by Darwin. The evidence was overwhelming; it is still being accumulated in the fields of palaeontology, anatomy, geology, zoology and embryology. The upholders of the theory of Special Creation had conviction based on faith but no proof. It only remained to explain how evolution worked, for scientists, unlike theologians, are expected to prove, not only that their theories are correct, but also why they are and how they work. For the unknown author of the Book of Genesis was no fool. He had a fertile imagination and a vivid style. The Special Creation of all species of plants and animals is a very reasonable assumption to make. The charge of foolishness lay at the doors of those who considered that it was wicked to question the assumption, and of those who refused to hear dispassionately the evidence produced in favour of a different theory.

The theory of evolution had many difficulties to face, for it is quite one thing to prove that something has occurred, and quite another to explain how and why. Special Creation is a rather beautiful, very simple explanation of an extraordinary phenomenon—the seemingly endless and lavish variety of nature, which either grips or swamps the imagination. It *is* easier to postulate a Creator who brought all these myriad and apparently dissimilar plants and animals into being. The difficulty of maintaining such an hypothesis only arose when, on closer inspection, all the dissimilarities vanished and the underlying relationships became apparent. Special Creation is a very crude supposition; evolution is very subtle, it demanded a feat of the imagination to conceive it, it demanded a feat of the intellect to explain it, and it demanded great courage to maintain it in the face of the established giants of custom and prejudice.

If the whole of the immense variety of plant and animal life has arisen by the process of evolution from one or a few prototypes, which came into existence through a combination of animate molecules hundreds of millions of years ago, how to account for it? What processes are quietly at work, unseen through endless time, moulding the lion's mane and unfolding the flower? What has set the bird apart from the lizard and man from the ape? How did the mouse part company from the whale, and the oak from the fern? It is understandable that man, faced with so much to explain, turned to a theory which demanded divine intervention. Evolution as a theory is not self-evident. It does not jump to the mind as an obvious explanation of the origin of species.

Darwin drew his conclusions from a series of observations: nature breeds extravagantly, with regard not to the fate of the individual, but to the survival of the species. Seeds and sperm, litters and spawn are reared and scattered in numbers which vastly exceed – should all or most survive – what is needed numerically to maintain the species. Yet by and large plant and animal populations remain constant; or are maintained, more precisely, at a level which is governed not by the fecundity of a parent stock but by the resources of the environment. Therefore, since there must be on the one hand a competitive struggle because there is neither food enough nor territory enough for all, and on the other hand a non-competitive struggle to survive such natural disasters as flood, drought, heat and cold, the vast majority must perish. The problem then is this: what is the selecting mechanism that decides whether the individual shall live or die?

Since all offspring, whether seed or egg, spawn or spore, differs in no matter how slight a degree from every other of its kind, there must be a struggle for existence which results in the survival of the fittest. This struggle does not necessarily, does in fact very rarely, involve hand to hand, or tooth and claw combat. It involves being slightly better fitted or adapted to the environment and therefore better equipped for defence or attack, better adapted to obtain water in the desert, better able to withstand heat or cold, fleeter of foot, faster on the wing, more observant or intelligent, more versatile, less specialized, more tenacious, less conservative. Furthermore, since at least some variations are inherited, and since the fittest survive, and since the fittest are more eligible as mates, by natural and sexual selection, there must be a constant improvement in the stock of every species; a constant tendency for a stock to become better adapted to its environment. The weak, the inferior and the misfits will be weeded out. Nature selects the best. This is Natural Selection—the selection of the best from among so many to survive and to hand on advantages so sifted to the next generation, which will be subjected in its turn to the same rigorous process of elimination.

Natural selection will, in any given locality when conditions are stable, hold a species true and beautifully balanced; in such a case it can be said to have a conservative effect. It can also, when conditions change, (and conditions always eventually change), select for survival those offspring which show a tendency in any direction which adapts them to the new circumstances; in such a case it can be said to have a dynamic and evolutionary effect.

Natural selection is responsible both for the minor differences between strains and sub-species, as well as for the major differences that, accumulating by infinitely small degrees, have created classes of plants and animals which to the casual observer bear no relationship one to another. But evolution by natural selection needs time; time to adapt and refine, time to replace and to render extinct. If 6,000 years were the age of the Earth then life must have been created; it could not have evolved. Before Darwin began to write this difficulty had been removed. The geologists had been at work, and their findings eliminated the last barrier to the general acceptance of the evolution of life as a basic scientific fact, to rank in importance with the *Principia* of Newton. The Earth was almost countless millions of years old.

The theory of the origin of species advanced by Darwin has weathered well. Its structure has remained intact. The evidence accumulated during a century of intensive research has done more to support than to weaken its argument.

Darwin, however, left certain questions open. He was obliged to do so for lack of evidence. In place of them he made certain broad common-sense assumptions, more particularly about inheritance. For Darwin, it should be recalled, although a contemporary of Mendel, was as unaware as the rest of his generation of that forgotten thesis, delivered and published in obscurity, which revealed the laws governing the physical basis of heredity.

At the risk of being repetitive, it seems pertinent at this juncture to run through in broad outline the main points of Darwin's thesis, in order to pinpoint that part of it which was left open. It will then be easier to follow the trend of modern elaborations and to study what is still controversial.

Firstly, he makes three observations. One: throughout the whole field of nature offspring, whether seed or egg, spore or sperm, are produced in such lavish quantities that all cannot survive. Two: that in spite of this lavish reproduction, animal and plant populations remain more or less static or at any rate never increase at the rate that their fertility theoretically permits. Three: all the offspring of all varieties differ from each other to some degree, however slight.

From these three observations Darwin made the following deductions. Since the majority of the offspring must perish, there must be a competition to survive involving a struggle to obtain space, air, sunlight, water, food, etc., and competition to secure a mate.

This part of the theory of natural selection has not been challenged. We can therefore let it stand as written, except that later on it will be necessary to consider who are the fittest to survive; what Darwin meant by fitness and what we, standing further away from the argument, could agree that this involves. But let us leave this quite separate problem aside for the moment and continue.

If the matter had been left there, that is to say at the point where each generation is cut down to size in the struggle to survive; if that were all, there would be no such thing as evolution. Each generation would be more or less a duplicate of its predecessor. There would be no advance. Exactly the same necessities of life would be repeated endlessly. So we come to the last point in the argument.

Since most variations are inherited, the advantages that the survivors possess over their contemporaries who perish will be handed on to the next generation. This is true whether reproduction is asexual or sexual. The only difference being that sexual reproduction introduces an additional factor—sexual selection, which fortifies natural selection by introducing a secondary struggle: the struggle to secure a mate. In any case the result is that by and large each generation will successively carry on the struggle on a slightly higher plane. The weak are always being weeded out, the best are always being preferred. Thus, there is theoretically, a continuous, however slight, improvement of condition, tone, adaptability, fitness. Varieties become more and more refined by their environment and perfectly adapted to it. If they scatter and come to be distributed over a widening area, the new conditions they meet will inevitably favour variations appropriate to those new conditions, which may differ slightly or totally from those prevailing in the original habitat. Thus families drift apart by almost insensible degrees, but over immensities of time these accumulate to create new strains, new varieties and even new species to be differentiated out of common ancestral stock.

This argument is still basic to the theory of evolution by natural selection despite the innumerable refinements, additions and changes in emphasis that have been made to it since it was originally advanced. It contains, however, one assumption which needs to be put under the microscope; not because its interpretation could invalidate the argument, but because the then state of knowledge allowed it to be advanced only in the most general way. We are no longer so restricted. The assumption of course was that most variations are inherited.

Evolution depends, we have already remarked, upon the efficient working of some process of inheritance. Darwin knew nothing about genetics or the heredity mechanism. He quite rightly based his assumption on a common-sense deduction from observation: that is to say, on the resemblance between members of the same species, members of the same varieties and members of the same families – as the relationship between members of a group becomes closer so do the resemblances become more obvious until the most striking resemblances of all occur, of course, between parents and offspring. Clearly a great deal was inherited. The problem was what? How much and how?

Chapter VI contained a summary of the present state of our knowledge of hereditary processes—the unique division of the sex-cells to ensure that they included a single complement of genes, the reshuffling of the genes due to the crossing-over device of the chromosomes, the recombinations and mutations of genes, the roles allotted to groups of genes and their intercommunication, dominance and recessiveness; finally fertilization and the joining together of two unlike halves to make a new whole.

All this post-Darwinian knowledge served to reinforce Darwinian theory. We are only in some doubt about the processes of inheritance. They are the subject of the remainder of this chapter. It is perhaps not difficult to understand how a mystery so great has defied unravelling for so long. Inheritance has brought man to his present physical evolutionary condition and all living things with him. It will take us to an as yet unknown destination: a destination that nature will devise or that man will devise for himself. Time spent on its study will not be wasted.

The problem is to discover what precisely the zygote—the fertilized egg of the female, the initial cell from which the whole individual is derived—inherits, and what it acquires from its environment. The human zygote receives twenty-three chromosomes from each parent, each of which contains thousands of genes. The physical, and an undetermined proportion of the mental basis of heredity is wrapped in these microscopic threads, to which must be added pre-natal nourishment supplied through the umbilical cord, and post-natal from the breast.

What happens after that—nurture as opposed to nature—depends upon a hundred and one other legacies which all offspring are heir to: legacies social and political, legacies economic, psychological and intellectual. All this is discussed later in this book. Here we are concerned only with nature; that is to say the psychosomatic heritage before the environment comes into play.

The problem has to be stated like this with the utmost precision, because it is over the physical basis of inheritance that a controversy has long raged. It is not, of course, in the least surprising that tempers become frayed. Inheritance is not only the very crux of evolution, it is a battle ground for biologists, educationalists, sociologists, eugenists, theologians and philosophers. What is inherited is quite simply the question of the century, although one would not know this from reading the popular – or even the unpopular – press. Whether or not the 'Brave New World' of Aldous Huxley or something like it is going to be our lot depends perhaps more on the imminent resolution of this problem than on our will to renounce or, at least, our resolution to stave off atomic war.

Let us, therefore, approach the problem with an open mind and with due respect to the consequences of our conclusions— or temporary lack of them— to our present knowledge and our present ignorance. There are, however, it should be stated frankly, no grounds for being consoled by our ignorance and doubts, for they will by all accounts shortly be dispelled. The precise mechanisms that regulate the inheritance of the beings that come so nakedly into this world will shortly be laid bare, with the very obvious result that we shall soon be in a position to decide what and who shall be allowed to cross its threshold and what physical and mental characters entitle would-be immigrants to be given passports into it.

The generally accepted, the orthodox view is that the sex-cells are handed on from generation to generation unchanged and uninfluenced by the lives of the organisms they inhabit. The body is a rather cumbersome and remote appendage. The sex-cells are totally withdrawn and unconcerned with the actions, the development, the thoughts and emotions, the feeding and drinking and training, the learning and achievements of the organism in which they reside. According to this theory evolution is confined to natural selection acting on new individuals haphazardly thrown up by the genes. The individual is, consequently, totally incapable of altering to the slightest degree the constitution of the offspring he is potentially capable of producing. The pattern is set. Within the sex-cells the genes will or will not mutate, will or will not cross over, and it is beyond the power of their 'carrier' to do anything to influence them.

Opinion, however, is divided, and although most biologists subscribe to the orthodox point of view, there are few who are prepared to be dogmatic about it. There is in fact a marked lack of evidence, which makes it seem strange that anything so definite as an orthodox point of view should have yet been formed.

Those who do not subscribe to this point of view are far from denying the importance of natural selection or the part played by gene mutations and gene reshuffling. They merely maintain that in addition to this raw material of evolution there is the part played by the inheritance of acquired characters. In other words, they hold that the sex-cells are not inviolate; that they are influenced by the body and mind of the organism they inhabit.

Theories of the inheritance of acquired characters are often rather contemptuously dubbed Lamarckian. Now it is not necessary to discuss here the theories and the works of Lamarck, for this would only create confusion, and there is no point in either defending or offending Lamarck. However, it is necessary to consider what other possibilities exist and what evidence is advanced in support of them, and this is best done by dealing separately with the three subtly related heresies that are attributed to him.

Firstly, there is the problem of the will.[2] It is maintained by some that willing effects a change in the body in response to it. The giraffe, wanting to reach the succulent topmost leaves of the topmost branches, wills a longer neck and achieves one; the athlete, wanting to jump higher or run faster, wills more spring in his muscles or a sounder wind and achieves them. It is scarcely doubted that the individual can will some sort of change in his constitution, or obtain it by constant striving or practice, but is the change that the will has effected heritable? Has the change been communicated to the sex-cells? Will the neck of the infant giraffe for this reason be longer? Will the athlete's son for this reason have a step that is sprightlier and a wind that is sounder? The idea is not ridiculous but no method has yet been devised that is capable of revealing inheritance of this kind. The absence of any sort of proof does not invalidate the idea, it merely puts it at a disadvantage vis-à-vis other ideas that can be confirmed or discarded. The idea should not be treated as naïve or absurd; it should be regarded as being in abeyance.

Secondly, there is the question of use and disuse. It is claimed that Lamarck falsely asserted that the extended use or disuse of any part of the body led, through the organism's interest or disinterest in maintaining it, to its improvement or deterioration. This is a much simpler problem to resolve, for in this case there is no need to postulate any intervention on the part of the organism. Natural selection working in the accepted way on the gene-complex will take care of this. If a bird or a fish, for instance, alters its mode of existence and has no longer any need to fly or to live under water, then the wings or the gills will deteriorate and gradually become vestigial. For, no longer possessing a survival value, they will not be kept up to that pitch of perfection at which valuable parts of the anatomy are constantly maintained. Similarly use will heighten perfection, because use implies need, and what is needed most is subjected to the most rigorous selection.

The third heresy attributed to Lamarck is the inheritance of the whole range of experience, knowledge, memory, arts and skills—the lessons of life—acquired by an individual organism during its lifetime. Obviously the richness of experience varies enormously between men and even more so between species. However, even very low forms of life appear to be capable of learning something. Are the genes in the sex-cells affected by the experiences of the body to which they are seconded? Men learn to read and write, to drive cattle, cars, trains and buses, to play pianos, chess and accordions, to operate computers, switchboards and on the Stock Exchange, to ride bicycles and camels, to paint pictures, to compose music, lyrics and stanzas; to sow, to saw, to stew, to sing and so on and so on. How much, if any, of all this is built into their children, so that when they are born they are, to some almost insensible degree, already readers, writers, drivers, operators, sowers, singers and so on? We do not know—yet.

This makes it all the more necessary to review what we do know, and to see whether any tentative conclusions can be drawn from that review. Is it possible that the characteristics acquired by the individual are 'leaked', even in a highly diluted form, into the sex-cells?

The fertilized egg grows and divides, and the resulting cells are differentiated with regard to the purposes for which they are intended. In the process the body is formed: brain, tissue, muscle, teeth, bone and, of course, gonads. In their turn the gonads will produce sex-cells when puberty is reached. The gonads are links in the chain of generations. Now the cells that are produced for the growth of the body and all its specialized parts, and the cells which are channelled off to the gonads for the good of the next generation are partitioned but not isolated, any more than the workers in different sections of a factory, or the inhabitants of a self-contained community. They must communicate, they must interact and they must be interdependent.

Although initially dormant the gonads are not insulated. They are dependent for their health and for their nourishment upon the health and condition of the entire body. As the child grows and reaches in turn puberty, adolescence and manhood, the accompanying production of sex-cells must lead to increasing physico-psychical-sexual interchange. The gonads being now active must require more nourishment and must, as a matter of common sense—let alone personal experience—maintain the most sensitive and volatile communications with every other part of the body; especially the brain, the glands, the central nervous system and the seats of the secondary sexual characters.

In view of all this it is hard to see how it can be maintained that the sex-cells are insulated from the living experiences of the body they inhabit. It would seem natural to assume, even in the absence of any other evidence, that characteristics acquired by parents would inevitably influence in some degree every part of their body and most particularly those parts which are the most sensitive.

It must, however, be admitted that evidence so far deduced in favour of the inheritance of acquired characteristics has not stood up to critical analysis. It is merely good sense to give both sides of the argument a hearing until the problem is resolved.

8 The Threshold of Humanity

OUT OF THE MAZE of natural selection there appears to be but one exit, and only man, from among all those extravagant millions of forms, has so far found it. And what is more, barely a century ago, he was still unaware of the nature and the setting of his unique achievement.

It is one thing to know where one is and quite another to know how one has arrived there. Yet in broad outline we know the answer to both these questions for, from the vantage point at which we stand, it is possible to look back and scan the whole extent of the valley of time past. The road leads out of the sea and ramifies in the shallows, on the mudflats and along the beaches; it edges its way overland clinging to water, up the mouths of rivers, beside the banks of inland lakes, or centred on pools, springs and water holes. It strikes deep into forests and arrows its way across grasslands, savannah, rolling hills, mountains and prairies, always casting off side roads, which in their turn ramify. The road is exploratory. It appears to have no set destination or purpose. It leaves in its wake an animated world teeming with life in new forms, new colours and new patterns. The air and the water, the trees, the long grass and the soil pulsate with its experiments.

We can pause and look back and follow its weaving path to the spot on which we are standing. What to make of it?

It is melancholy because so many of its experiments are extinct; it is enthralling because of its vitality. It is melancholy because everything that comes to life is destined to die; it is enthralling because it is constantly renewing itself and constantly inventing. It is melancholy because we are aware of the futile paths that life has often taken and yet invigorating because of life's evident success.

Is it more to be wondered at that we have arrived at the present zenith of evolution at all, or that the way had to be so devious? Surely if there had been a guiding mind there would have been fewer abortive experiments? For the way up to the eminence on which we are standing is littered with the bones of the extinct, the bizarre, the futile, sad, absurd and hideous failures. And apart from that, our contemporaries are to all appearances living fossils.

What our gaze reveals is so fantastic that it deserves not only to be observed but also to be analysed.

All those ramifications that led nowhere, all those blind alleys and culs-de-sac were 'decisions' taken to exploit a particular physical or climatic environment. They were shots in the dark, some of which had extraordinary success, and not only survived but dominated the earth for thousands, or millions or even tens of millions of years. Yet from the moment of their branching off from the main road their destiny was extinction. Neither size, nor strength, nor numbers availed them anything. They were off at a tangent or on a false scent, and their days, however numerous, were numbered.

The first chapters of this book are intended, among other things, to remind us of the devious yet constructive ways that evolution has pursued and discarded or pursued and persevered with on its marathon journey. Thus equipped we can look back and criticize or look back and dissect. Let us be wise after the event in order that we may be wiser before the next one.

What conclusions can be drawn from a careful scanning of those long vistas of the past? We, ourselves, are a remnant of those that set out on this journey and of those who have died and are still dying on the road. We are a remnant and yet we are accompanied by millions of familiar and unfamiliar contemporaries who are set apart from us for one biological reason or another. We cohabit the entire surface of the earth, on the land and in the sea, in the air and under the earth; useful and useless, friend and foe, domestic and wild, visible and invisible, plant and insect, beast and fish and fowl.

What is it essential for an organism to be, not for mere survival, but for survival charged with potential, further evolution?

(i) Complex — Molecules are a coalescence of atoms; cells a coalescence of molecules. Patterns are formed and these patterns provide new possibilities, possibilities which do not become apparent until coalescence takes place. The new whole is always more than a sum of its parts. In their turn cells coalesce. Single-celled organisms survive but they are incapable of further evolution. Therefore, the joining together first of elementary and later of complex particles is the raw material of evolution.

(ii) Mobile — Plant life took a rooted, static path. This path has much to recommend it. Its success has been phenomenal. Might there not be greater evolutionary potential in organisms that are content to draw their sustenance from air and sun and earth, unencumbered by gross material ambition and undisturbed by the traffic and rivalry of animal occasions? How big with thought the trees and flowers might have been. Yet immobility has not been their blessing but their bane. They have had no challenge. Motionless they wait their separate fates, incapable of more defence than sting or prickle, and rooted to their separate spots and plots, incapable of concerted action. Their failure is dual: no challenge and no co-operation.

(iii) Terrestrial— Life originated in the sea. The land was colonized with great difficulty. The sea is an easier medium, undergoing but slight changes of temperature between day and night and between winter and summer. But marine life is unchanging, monotonous and uncatastrophic. Fish have greater possibilities than plants of co-operation, and they have greater challenges to face, but the challenge is not so strong nor the need for co-operation so intense as on the land.

Can it not then be deduced for a start that evolution favours those of its children who are complex individually, who are capable of further complexity by co-operation among themselves, and who by reason of their mobility and of their environment are spurred on by threat and by challenge?

Some 70 million years ago the reptilian domination of the earth abruptly ended. For 150 million years this most stupendous branch of animal life, stupendous in size, stupendous in the duration of its supremacy, was undisputed master. The reptiles satisfied the conditions we have so far felt justified in deducing. They were complex, mobile and terrestrial. The reason for their disappearance (apart from a few humble specimens that are still with us), cannot be stated with certainty. The explanations offered have already been enumerated. What concerns us here is the nature of their successors. Looking back again down the roads that sinew their way to the eminence on which we stand, we can see that a broad highway seething with an extinct reptilian life leads nowhere, and that out of the main trunk road shot a new branch leading more or less directly to where we stand.

The new shoot was a very humble thing as things usually

are in the beginning. Whether this new shoot brought about or contributed to the decline of the reptiles, or whether the reptiles declined through some inherent deficiency of their own, we do not know.

All we can say with certainty is that the reptile was supplanted by the mammal some 70 million years ago. What title have we mammals to our supremacy?

If we correctly deduced that the three essentials of continued evolution are that an organism be complex, mobile and terrestrial, we only, in fact, condemn to obscurity the vegetable and the fish. No animal can become more mobile or more terrestrial, but it can become more complex. Is, then, the mammal more complex than the reptile, and if so, in what ways? It is going to be rewarding to try to answer this question, for the replies we receive are going to throw a flood of light on man.

To be correct it should be stated that mammals are divisible into three sub-classes; one of them, in spite of its high-sounding name—monotremata—can be written off immediately. It contains, rather pathetically, the spiny anteater and the duck-billed platypus; nothing more need be said about THEM. Another sub-class—somwhat less disreputable—the marsupialia, to which belong the opossum and the kangaroo, is dying out. Opposed to these pale, thin, rotting branches of mammalian stock is the sub-class of the placental mammals to which we triumphantly belong, along with the whale and the monkey, the lion, the donkey, the mouse and thousands of others. But to pose the question again, what title have we, mammals, to our supremacy?

From all other living things we are distinguishable in three apparently quite separate ways: firstly, we are hairy and warm-blooded, which results in our having a constant internal temperature; secondly, the female of the species secretes milk; thirdly, we have large skulls capable of housing out-size brains. And, as everyone knows, the placental mammals superimpose on this framework of distinctions one other: the young are nourished within the womb and emerge helpless from it. The three corners which support the pyramid of mammalia, and so of man's supremacy are these: internal physical equilibrium, prolonged care of the young, brain potential.

Wherein lies the importance of these? To proceed carefully and avoid lengthy entanglement it is as well, at this stage, to deal curtly with each.

Warm-bloodedness is a condition upon which the other two distinctions depend for their proper functioning. It provides a stable, internal environment which permits a constant and persistent, day in and day out, physical effort, uninterrupted by hibernation or spasmodic response to weather. This all-importantly means that the brain is provided with a milieu climatically conditioned to its needs, for, as we shall see, the brain is fragile and will not survive rigours that the body can support. This dictates that when mammals die they die brain first— which is merciful. Our Achilles heel is in our head.

That is the first point. Secondly, prolonged care of the young.

The individual is mortal; the species must not be. Normally in nature, plant and animal alike ensure the immortality of their kind by producing offspring prodigiously in excess of what the environment could carry if all survived. The principle being, sensibly enough, that it is better to err on the safe side and produce too many than too few. Hence eggs and spawn and spore and seed are laid and scattered in countless millions. It is a wasteful method, judged by human husbandry, but it works. It works but it suffers from a grave limitation which is fatal to ambition; the greater the number, the slighter the care bestowed on each. Seed is not placed, it is cast. Aim is not taken, shots are fired at random in the dark. If enough seed is cast, some will fall on good ground; if enough shots are fired some will hit the target. The grave limitations in the efficiency of this method are these: quantity is given precedence over quality, and laying of egg or spawn does not render the female of the species sufficiently dependent for sufficiently long. For extended female helplessness is, oddly enough, in a world where towering strength is valued above all else, the key to social evolution. With simple logic the helpless offspring needs a dependable mother, and a dependable mother needs a dependable mate; the family group is born.

The feeding and the nursing is inevitably accompanied by instruction. Imitation by the younger of the elder has begun. From that moment on, progeny will no longer be a bundle of imperative instincts. Evolution has made a great jump forward in the dark, and struck a new line of advance; social tradition is laid open for exploration. Only we, now 70 million years later, are able to gauge fully its import and its potential.

The egg on its own is not enough. True it provides a modicum of safety and a store of nourishment, but it is not educational. Reptiles have the lamentable habit of laying and leaving, and eggs are a source of food to predator as well as to occupant. The womb has no equal as a residence for helpless things. It puts a greater strain upon the female, but what is that when laid in balance against the success of the species?

It is true that the birds have broken with their reptilian ancestry and bestow post-natal care, but they lack the third mammalian distinction—room for a brain. The requirements of flight are so exacting that the body is subservient to it. Wings take precedence over heads. Care of young ensures their survival; it is not enough in itself to ensure their dominance.

This third distinction, the large skull, is the mammals' unrivalled glory. A large skull permits, of course, a large brain. The brain, however, may not develop. It is a practical organ like any other, and its growth depends upon the practical demands that are made upon it. Mammals do not as a rule make many demands, so that the brain potential is never realized, and the cat, the dog and the whale have gone their way unintellectually.

If we cannot trace with a sure hand the path that our ancestors took through this zoological labyrinth, it is not surprising. It is not much more than a hundred years ago that we discovered that there was a path at all. And although it is wise not to assume anything, it is permissible to speculate within the frontiers of the knowledge we possess. We rove back over the past, not only because of the fascination of uncovering our beginnings, but also in order to open a window on the present and — not to be forgotten for a moment — our future.

Among the mammals is an order called the primates. Until recently it was not numerically very strong. It is an order which contains monkeys, apes and men, and is therefore worth exploring. Its members are markedly dissimilar, both from other mammals and between themselves.

All primates were originally arboreal creatures and life in the trees developed in them, as habitats will, certain specific qualities. Firstly, on the ground a long nose goes a long way towards ensuring an animal a long life; in the air it is sight, not smell, that counts: the primates quietly allowed their noses to atrophy. As the snout recedes and flattens into the face (for want of an occupation), the eyes combine to give stereoscopic vision: sight in depth. It is scarcely necessary to emphasize the importance of improved sight to an acrobatic anthropoid ape. Any arboreal ape with bad vision would come to a bad end. Down to earth though we are now, the sharp eyesight we learnt in those most ancient days has never left us and is one of the few physical attributes that man has sharpened in historical times.

The other quality the arboreal primate evolved was two-leggedness. All the primates' relations, no matter how far back, have four or more legs— or none. Four is an obviously sensible number as far as legs are concerned. They provide symmetry and balance. Two legs are an absurdity, and no creature thus malformed would ever have survived if it had not learnt in the trees the advantages of transforming forelegs into arms and hands. If one can move about on two legs it is uneconomic to use four. The arms are released for swinging and the hands for handling. The hand loses its claws and is transformed from an aid to locomotion and killing, to an organ of acute sensation.

The eyes saw more deeply and the forelimbs handled more easily. The former looked at, and speculated about what the latter picked up, turned over and felt. Hand and eye were off on a great adventure. There was room at the top, in the skull, for the brain to develop.

Furthermore, the primates superimposed two revolu-tionary breeding refinements: seasonal sex went by the board and the size of litters was reduced until eventually it fell to the ideal norm of one.

Animals congregate for various reasons, but the herd and flock are often loose organizations which are sometimes spasmodic. The absence of a rutting season among primates, i.e., no marked seasonal fluctuation in female willingness or attraction, reduces male inclination to stray. The family is held together permanently.

The advantages attendant upon having only one offspring at a time are less obvious. The pre-natal advantage lies in the elimination of competition in the womb. Struggle at this stage puts high survival value on precocity and high speed of growth. Pre-natal precocity is individually valuable to the possessor of it, but socially harmful and deleterious to the species, for in the course of time, by the usual slow processes of natural selection, precocity becomes more and more dominant; the period of gestation is speeded up, and maturity is hastened. But there is nothing to be gained from rapid development. In the primates, and particularly in man, helplessness is prolonged, and prolonged helplessness means prolonged care; hence a prolonged education, and a more varied social life in the family, group or troop. Extended immaturity means a long childhood unencumbered by sexual distractions, and the exhaustion of vital energies that that entails. The mind, instead of being hurried into action, will be given time to unfold.

There are no glaringly obvious differences that set us apart. With our common ancestor, evolution had already solved all the major anatomical problems set at the beginning of time, when atoms were first juggling into strange cohesions. We and our cousinly anthropoids are nature's masterpiece, with a blood circulation that ensures a constant internal temperature; with four limbs: two for movement and two for manipulation. We have a nervous system to keep us informed about our environment, and a spinal cord topped with a knob, called the brain, to control the functions of the body and eventually to speculate, to reason and to analyse. Our eyes have come round to the front of the head to give sight in depth, and the nose is reduced; sight has preference over smell. The whole is generalized. There are no special weapons of defence or attack, no horns or antlers, no tail or trunk, no aggressive teeth; no hoof or claw, no scales, no wings, no armour.

It is odd to look back over hundreds of millions of years of lavish and bizarre experiment with brontosaurus, hippopotamus and the bumble bee, to realize that all that was needed was a creature resembling a chimpanzee.

Such is the triumph of generalization. For specialization is the bane of life. Each attempt to concentrate upon any particular objective is fatal. Each branch that shoots out from the main trunk of evolution displays immense initiative and is pregnant with huge possibilities, but possibilities which are limited. To grow out on a branch is to fly at a tangent and to be out on a limb, and there is no way back. A specialization once made is a commitment for all eternity. Whatever its destiny it inevitably bears, stamped on its anatomy, the evidence of a special 'decision' made no matter how long ago. It will perfect itself ultimately within its special limitations. It will die out or go its timeless way beautifully adapted to a certain way of life; the lion for killing, the fish for swimming, the bird for flight. They have their rewards. It is possible even to envy them sometimes, sleepless at night under the threat of isolation, poverty or war.

Man, however, from a certain standpoint broke this rule by specializing in his turn when he put his trust and all his eggs in the basket of his brain. That brain enabled his most simian ancestors to go their way naked and apparently defenceless. He who was not equipped by nature with claws enough to dig a hole, or tail to swish even a fly, would one day make tools and weapons enough to do these things, and more. For the brain, which is physiologically a specialization, is psychologically a generalization, and it enables its possessor, uncluttered by the paraphernalia of defence or attack, to pick up and discard the things it needs at will. And some young primate tens of millions of years ago, picking up a stick or stone armed himself for the fray. It was the first step in that long technical march that will lead us very soon now to death or to the stars.

What is man? It is hard to say; no simple definition will suffice. When man diverges from the primate line and goes off on a track of his own, he does so with no particular flourish. He shares this apparent peculiarity with all his predecessors. New species leave too few traces of their transition for them to be found. It is difficult to explain this except by pictorial analogy. A deviation is always dangerous, usually fatal. There is a very flimsy, temporary, transitory bridge between one species and another. It must be crossed as quickly as possible, because during the passage the experiment is exposed – like an advance across a stretch of open ground. It is hardly surprising that of the few fossils we find, none record that brief, perilous crossing.

Man's distinction lies within himself in unmeasurable qualities. Physical evolution which had been at work with endless time and unimaginable patience, fashioning every possible combination of cellular organisms, and bestowing on each the same tireless care, with him had reached its end. Nothing had been too fantastic or too absurd, too clumsy or too elegant, too banal or too bizarre. The octopus, the jellyfish, the orchid, the giraffe and the worm all evolved their separate ways, and all were given equal opportunity to gain renown.

We look out now over our 'modern' world, over the sea and over the reserves of nature, and observe the slight remains of the countless millions who set out on this immense journey. Maybe experiments are still going on. We cannot tell for the pace of nature is too soft-footed and too slow. What we can say with a fair degree of certainty, however, is that evolution as we know it, as it has revealed itself in these pages so far, has ended in all probability for ever. The growth of the brain is, of course, the evidence on which this statement relies for support.

It does not seem to be merely a human bias to assume that a brain needs a body in the same way that a general needs an army and a government a country.

Any body would do; but for the brain to be able to realize its potential it must have a particular body, in the same way that no matter how potentially brilliant a general or an administration may be, both are inevitably frustrated by, respectively, untrainable soldiers and ineducable citizens. We have already discussed what these qualities appear to be: sensitivity, warm-bloodedness, hands and stereoscopic vision. It might seem to us who possess all these things and more, and are apt, therefore, to take them for granted, that evolution might have hit on us as a solution a little sooner without going through all these contortions. Evolution could not have been planned although from now on, since we are aware of it, it can be. Evolution was endless trial and error, where time was so long that errors did not matter, unless they mattered in the sense that they were essential to what followed. The errors are the furniture of the earth as well as our relations and our nourishment.

Some of the primates were conservatives; they kept their tails and to the trees, others came down and became anthropoid and hominoid.

What brought them down? It was as fateful a decision as that other made 200 million years earlier when the first fish floundered over the shallows and lay breathing on some receding Permian shore. Was the climate responsible? Long droughts mean shrinking forests and turn the land over to long grass—savannah. Animals get trapped in shrinking forests, as fish can be trapped in drying ponds or lakes or inland seas. Or was the change less dramatic and less catastrophic? It could have been a choice rather than a compulsion. The ground is invitingly close from low branches. It can reward a visit; it can need to be visited to retrieve dropped food and clumsy, fallen infant. The switch from tree to ground might have been gradual. Only slight physical adjustments needed to be made: the legs to be straightened and strengthened, the buttocks to be enlarged, a slight modification of the bones connecting the head with the back of the neck to shift the head further back on the shoulders. First the shuffling gait and then, by degrees, the stance erect. The deed is done.

That is all very well, but on the ground the primate has a very special problem and challenge to meet. Animals, by and large, are either herbivorous or carnivorous; the former either make themselves inconspicuous or are built for defence or for flight, the latter are built for the spring and the stealth of attack. Consequently the jungle floor could not have been a carefree playground for succulent little monkeys or even for big nourishing ones. The predator, if able to judge, would have seen no future for that would-be man. He must have been something of a jungle joke on his two legs, unable to defend himself, unable to run, unable to attack, without hoof or horn, or claw or fighting teeth. But he had hands and a brain and excellent vision, so with stick and stone and embryonic social conscience, he, an ape of destiny, was opening a way to the top.

But where is man in all this? What is clearly ours that we can firmly grasp? The answer is not, at first sight, reassuring for physically there is very little; just one thing, the chin. Nurse your chin in the cup of your hand, it is your only badge of humanity.

When man goes down those endless corridors of time in

search of his beginnings, he looks in ancient gravels. He can hope to find only those few things that have escaped the long wash and friction of time: the skulls and the bones of his ancestors and of their victims, the tools and the weapons he left of bone and of stone, and then finally, the accumulated ashes of his fires and middens. All these need patient sifting. Through several hundred thousand years all else has perished.

Did our anthropoid ancestors descend from the trees to carry on the same fight on ground-level for food and terri-tory? What was, in fact, the nature of the struggle?

These questions have highly topical overtones. They will be boarded now within the framework of the rest of this study.

We who live in cities do not appear from our behaviour to be entirely at home in them. The country must still be pulling at our ancestral strings. So we go when we can, when we are allowed and freed, when we retire; for week-end or for holiday or for good, in search of what our urban life has filched. When we do this we see nature's endless variety of colour and form, of pattern and movement, of light and shade; the unquestioning simplicity of life in the air, under water and on and under the earth, and we are apt to compare the seeming fairness of that life with the ugliness of our own, and to wonder what has befallen us that we should have lost such simple harmony and untroubled grace. Have we not found harmony and left filth? Do we not, in fact, befoul everything we touch? We seem to have lost contact with nature and with that natural state of things which our in-genuity spends its time obliterating.

This is an extreme point of view. It leaves out of account quite as much as it includes. It is equally possible to swing to the other extreme and to see man as a comparatively benign instrument, in a malign world.

The technique of conflict at its most merciful is hardly benign. At its most cruel, it is far more terrible than mere murder for self-preservation. There is the familiar example of the cat who is not content to kill the mouse for nourishment, but must also torture it for fun. There are the young whelks who are born in solid capsules where their only food is one another. There are the solitary bee-killing wasps which kill their victims for the few drops of honey in their crops.[1]

Julian Huxley emphasizes the same extreme point of view, but he extends it over the whole evolutionary front.

Natural selection, in fact, though like the mills of God in grinding slowly and grinding small, has few other attributes that a civilized religion would call divine. It is efficient in its way — at the price of extreme slowness and extreme cruelty. But it is blind and mechanical, and accordingly its products are just as likely to be aesthetically, morally and intellectually repulsive to us as they are to be attractive.[2]

Moreover, it can perfectly well be demonstrated that horror and ruthlessness are the rule and not the exception throughout the whole of nature and that even the plant world is not exempt.

These carnivorous plants produce splendid material for the ciné-camera ... All the life, the activity, the almost reasoning intelligence that films about plants disclose go on around us all the time in real life. Only the human eye fails to show us these vegetable movements which ... lay open another sphere of conflict and victory, of struggle and achievement, of hard work and short cuts to success, in short of the life in a community very like our own.[3]

Man, subject to the tyranny of his eyes, is incredulous or forgetful of all to which they do not bear witness. The jungle is far from most centres of civilization; subterranean and submarine life are concealed from him; a microscopic plant and insect world lie at his feet but they are normally invisible. Most living things avoid man with good reason; for the rest, those that are near and visible, he dissects, domesticates and devours at his leisure and at his discretion.

The superficial beauty of nature should be revelled in but it should neither be romanticized nor denied. If venomous struggle there be beneath, it should be brought to light and questioned. Are we all the victims of an elaborate gamble; all subject to the hazard of mutations and the meaningless and rigorous examination of natural selection? Are time and accident the arbiters of evolution, and are all our treasured values a mockery? If natural selection demands vast wastes of time and waste of life, and if accidental mutations are the measure of its purposes, and man and midge its feckless progeny, then all is immaterial to the individual for all is preordained.

This argument has much to recommend it. It may be pursued relentlessly, gathering force from every point of view, for all living things are subject to injury or destruction from three directions: from other species who prey upon them, from members of their own species in competition with them and from accident. These three causes prevent the majority of offspring from ever reaching maturity and dying 'natural' deaths. If there were no accidents and no struggle for survival and all the offspring of all species reached maturity, there would shortly be no room to live or even move on the land or in the seas, and nature would become a crawling, seething, stinking mass. But this is in any case an impossible hypothesis, since all animals and some plants depend for their survival on the food that the destruction of others provides, so that the stinking mass would shortly stop crawling and seething and become a dead one. This means that if the lion ever lies down with the lamb, it will be a suicide pact, and they will be lying down to die.

The many are always dying that the few may live, and if the few survive on account of their possessing some evolutionarily valuable advantage over their rivals—which must be so—then the whole revolting digestive process is not in vain. Appetite, remorseless appetite, is an incontrovertible law of life as evolved at least on this Planet. All living things seem to be born to fight, to reproduce and to die. Then why, one is entitled to wonder, is the instinct of self-preservation so strong when death is the purpose rather than the accident? To which we can certainly make reply, that any organism devoid of the will to live would not be present to bear witness to its unenduring peculiarity.

Is life really as vile as that? Some of us have chosen, not unnaturally, to invest it with an idealism which is completely foreign to it and therefore to us too, since we all have a common source.

If all animals were totally individualistic, and if every member of every species lived in complete isolation, then total war and total savagery would be inevitable, normal and endemic. The palm of evolution would go to the strongest, the most aggressive, the most violent and the most cruelly armed. Might would be right and no creature—least of all man—would have survived who questioned a law so obvious. The individual would need to be self-sufficient whether mammoth, monkey, mole or mouse, and would only meet one of its own or any other kind at mealtimes.

But nowhere, in fact, does one find such a state of affairs. Animals live in flocks and packs and herds for all or part of their lives; for the rest they nest or pair or group. In a word, animals are social beings. And as soon as two or more creatures come together, for no matter what purpose, the law that there is no law, is broken. For social life inevitably involves co-operation no matter how perfunctory or temporary it may be. Natural selection is acquitted of the charge of unmitigated brutality. The co-operation of which we are speaking is, of course, co-operation in self-interest, but it is self-interest with a nick taken out of it. Its absoluteness has been compromised.

If, however, co-operation were not advantageous it would never have passed the rigorous tests of natural selection. Animals which co-operated, and in so doing compromised their absolute selfishness, would have been eliminated and there would have been no social beings and therefore no society, let alone civilizations.

It is undeniable that mutual aid — at least within certain fields of activity and restricted groupings — has survival value.

Mutual aid, once resorted to, brings in its train a grave psychological complication. When self-sufficiency is king, one grabs one's dinner and one damns the rest; but co-operation, however primitively and reluctantly it may be practised, introduces divided impulses. A split, a crack appears because of a duality of attitude. For on the one hand, there is mate and offspring, member of the same troop or herd, totem, nation, class; and on the other there is the excluded world. Towards the one it is necessary to show restraint and consideration, towards the rest hostility. Animals have to reconcile themselves to this split when they form their groupings. The social organization, however loose, curbs individualism and imposes obedience. At the same time it creates inhibitions, for there must be discipline and therefore a chain of command, an accepted tradition, division of labour between young and old, male and female.

Nature is taming itself and being schooled; learning the value of co-operation. Learning? Think back over the pages of this book. Are not co-operation, coagulation, coalescence, complexity and congregation the themes that have been running through the variations of evolution?

The lowly atom is a co-ordination of functions in which proton, neutron and electron play their co-operative roles. Every molecule is a joining of forces, a society of atoms, achieving in unity a complexity which individually could not be achieved. Every cell is a hive of industry depending for its survival on the multiplicity of its interrelationships. Every organism that is multicellular is organized as a society wherein all the parts contribute to the growth of the whole. Every moving, living thing is an obvious example illustrating the absolute value of co-operation. No atom, molecule, cell or creature could survive if it were at war within itself. Every step that evolution takes on the path of complexity is a victory for self-discipline in which the individual, whatever it is, foregoes a measure of its individuality for the sake of the organism of which it is a part.

When we view the animal from this standpoint, certain of its aspects come into proper focus.

It is immediately obvious that since co-operation can succeed, can have survival value, can be 'naturally selected' *within* an organism, then it should be equally possible for it to be equally successful when it is practised *outside* an organism. For since living things combine to become the entities that they are, however complex the part and however complex the whole, then it is to be expected that the individual organisms so formed will in their turn benefit from repeating the process on a different level. Thus the individual should follow the example set by its own constitution and form new patterns of group, flock and herd co-ordination.

Appetite and aggression are none the less real. Co-operation, however perfect, will never banish appetite and may never stop aggression. Besides, even if it could eradicate them both it could only do so gradually and in the knowledge of their existence. They are too ingrained. They are transferred to more and more distant objects, but distances on a circular planet are limited by circumference. The object of hatred can only retreat so far.

But co-operation is essential to lasting success and however much the individual may baulk at having to share its dinner, and however reluctant the strong may be to contribute to the maintenance of the weak, finally the adjustment is oddly necessary for all concerned.

No doubt great individual power can achieve great individual, temporary success, but it leaves no trace in the exacting geological strata of evolution. The race does not go to the aggressive but to the co-operative.

If this is true, it suggests a rather more subtle possibility: if strenth lies in co-operation, is it not justifiable to deduce that the unarmed, lacking individual power, co-operate more fully in order to achieve in large numbers what is denied them singly or in small groups? Great individual strength inhibits co-operation. The race does not go to the strong or even to the swift, but to the defenceless who achieve power by that most highly tested evolutionary means—mutual aid.

Perhaps we have come full cycle here.

The common ancestors of anthropoid ape and man came down from the trees and abandoned the safety trees provided, either gradually or catastrophically. In either case they came down to an earth in a condition that by jungle standards was suicidal.

When they descended they undoubtedly brought a social organization down with them. Our contemporaries and their descendants who remained up there (and who are up there still), are highly social. So rash and momentous a descent must have added considerably to their need to enlarge and improve their social organization.

Interdependence initially was no doubt entirely defensive. There is no need to endow their sociability with altruistic motives. However, once resorted to, social life brings into being all sorts of secondary attitudes and attributes. Collaboration imposes restraints in proportion to its benefits.

This is not a romantic picture. The partial sacrifice of the individual to the group does not eliminate tooth and claw struggle, but it does shift it on to another level, and tends to make it local rather than general. The group instead of the individual is the offensive/defensive unit. The enemy is no longer every beast, whether or not of one's own species, who crosses one's path in the jungle, but only those which do not belong to the accepted grouping. One has friends and foes, not just foes.

Each grouping becomes the acknowledged occupant of a certain area whose boundaries are normally respected. Such an area is known to naturalists as 'territory'. The frontier is no human invention—it is as well for man to know what he has inherited and what, if anything, he has done with it.

It is only comparatively recently that it has been established, beyond any possibility of doubt, that society and territorialism are universal characteristics of all animal life.

Dragonflies and giraffes, birds and fish, sea-lions, grass-hoppers and monkeys alike are committed in their different ways to social life and territorial instincts. Territory varies in size from square miles of jungle to a few inches of sand, but its significance is not proportionate to its size. Birds, for instance, occupy nesting areas, appropriated by the males, guarded by them and insuring them mates. The territory 'belongs' to the pair on the ground and in the air above it. Similarly dragonflies divide up a stretch of river; fish, a parcel of water. Not only does the superficial area vary with the species, but also the duration of the occupance—birds for several months, dragonflies for a day.

The territorial instinct appears to be deeply rooted, since it is found in the most diverse species. Its value has no simple, universal foundations. It is an effective way of rationing the available food supply; it is an effective system of birth control—a male without territory is unable to find a mate. It is an effective way to reduce conflict to the minimum. It effectively provides an ayslum for mating pairs to rear young. A territory, moreover, is a home and a home gives status, and status enables the individual to develop unimpeded its personality. The owners of territory are put on their mettle, mood is refined to a balance of contending sensations.

As far as our observations reveal, territory is always de-fended and nearly always defended successfully. Territory may be held by any grouping, family, troop or herd, and within any species disputes are nearly always caused by boundary intrusion. Frontiers are marked in the most diverse ways: by the mood of the occupant, by urination, by song—to mention a few.

The primate, of course, is no exception.

In this chapter it has been possible to touch lightly on a few of the most outstanding qualities that we anthropoids have

inherited from our nearest, and from our most distant ancestors. As the patient study of animal behaviour is pursued, so
should we be able the better to fathom the complications of
instinct, mood, learning and memory that animals display.
The better we understand animal behaviour, the better shall
we understand ourselves. When we are made aware of the
antique beginnings of so much of our human behaviour, we
may begin to see ourselves in a new light.

Self-knowledge, embryonic though it is, is the measure of
our humanity; for superimposed on all the extraordinary
ramifications of animal social life we have a brain and a mind
of unheard of proportions. It is about these that the next
chapter revolves.

9 Mind

Why should mind have a body? The answer may well run: to mediate between it and other minds.

Sherrington

IN THE LAST few chapters an attempt was made to trace the evolution of living matter from its inorganic origins to man. Although there must have been a variety of transitional forms, it is the cell, an agglomeration of complex molecules, that first shows evidence of recognizable life, and it is with the cell that we are still concerned when we study ourselves. Cells are the bricks of which all living matter of which we have cognizance is composed. Cells singly, and then cells in progressively more ambitious groupings, have continued through perhaps 1,500 million years, to experiment with patterns, and there is absolutely no reason to suppose that they have reached the end of their evolutionary tether.

Innumerable patterns must have failed to demonstrate the slightest survival value, and so the record of their existence has been lost for ever. We know, however, thanks to geologist, palaeontologist, embryologist, and comparative anatomist a great deal about those patterns that were successful: that is to say, those that survived and reproduced their kind over a sufficiently long period to leave considerable traces of their passage in the sedimentary strata of the past.

We and our animal contemporaries are thus supplied with a family tree. Details remain to be filled in, but the outline is clear and unmistakable.

When we scan with a flick of the imagination the variety

of nature, extant and extinct, so drawn into a comprehensive relationship, we are able to speculate about evolution in many new ways, and particularly about man's dominant position and how it has been achieved.

From among the many deductions we can make, one stands out which is germane to the argument of this chapter, it is this: all living things adapt themselves to their environment; every species finds a niche in nature. The niche may be vacant or it may be one from which it is necessary to eject an occupant. Every room in the house of nature is full, and the occupants are all fitted—have fitted and adapted themselves—to the space available.

The long-term result of adaptation to environment is survival at a cost, and the price of survival is the abandonment of further evolution. All our perfectly adapted contemporary animal relations have put survival first and paid the price. Every pattern of cells, every animal and vegetable, achieved its place in nature by excelling in some way or other; all living things, by virtue of the competition between them and of the exigencies of the environment, were forced to specialize. To fail to specialize is to court disaster, for to generalize—to be a jack of all trades and master of none—invites defeat in every field.

On the face of it, it is suicidal to possess a generalized body in a world of specialists. Yet on a long view generalization is the only way through the maze of evolution. All the blind alleys have been explored and occupied, and those who took them can be seen carefully tended in the cages of any zoo. It must, however, have been a very close shave, and it is no wonder that so rash a thing as man appeared but yesterday upon the stage of nature.

But how is man so different? And what is so fatal, on a long view, about specialization?

Evolution concentrates on perfecting the body in detail and in parts. It subscribes to the immediate and unique needs of each species; for species are circumscribed by their environment, that is to say, by geography, by climate and by the general biological situation which includes the availability of food, room and shelter. In pursuit of this end the existing resources are divided and the existing species adapted to exploit the environment with the minimum of conflict and the maximum of efficiency. We animals are guests on a planet which is our host. We may presume only so far on its hospitality, a hospitality that is dispensed provided it is not abused.

Evolution fits us, therefore, into the pattern of nature's economy. It sharpens or flattens the teeth, shortens or lengthens the beak, softens or hardens the pads of the feet, tenses the crouch and times the spring, covers with feathers or hair, gives wing or fin, makes carnivorous, insectivorous and herbivorous. It camouflages, speeds, toughens, protects and defends.

The feast that nature provided was divided. Those who partook during all those hundreds of millions of years before the coming of man, and all those who partake now and are not human, depended upon a particular skill to justify and ensure the continuity of their share.

But adaptations once made could never be relinquished. Every perfection of parts is a step on a journey with a one-way ticket. The more successful, the more perfect and delicate the adaptation, the more condemned was its possessor to persist in it.

There was only one way through this maze of enticing blind alleys, and we, as we know to our benefit and to our cost, took it. The brain had to be enlarged. This is a specialization too—but a specialization which provides general not particular advantages. It is a specialization to end specializations. For the brain by its enlargement enables its possessor to manufacture the parts and things it needs instead of having to wait on the fortuitous mutation that may bring about their growth. All animals except man are unencumbered by possessions and incapable of accumulating them. Man makes and accumulates and discards at will all the tools he deems that he requires for the complexity of living; all other animals painfully over millenia grow their undiscardable paws and pads and horns and tails and bits and pieces.

By evolutionary time standards human brain growth has been explosively fast. Such speed lends weight to the argument that our ancestors were forced by the long Pliocene drought—by the shrinking forest—to make do on the ground, and to answer the challenge that life on it issued, or to perish. The primate still confines himself to the tropical forests. It is not difficult to understand the dilemma of our ancestors whose *Lebensraum* was century by century being reduced by the encroaching savannah and the shrivelling trees.

The primates are, with few exceptions, completely generalized. The sight of one is enough immediately to pose a question—how did they survive the hungry pandemonium of African nights? It is worth making an effort of the imagination and projecting one's mind and transporting one's body back. Even with all your modern wit and cunning added, what would you have done when the sun set and the night fell and the stars came out over the jungle? When nature was stilled; when the eye could not be closed for safe sleeping; when the wind or the serpent or the lion rustled the grasses and the high safety of the trees had vanished?

The primates had no defensive parts. Slow accumulation of favourable mutations generation by generation would provide eventually a physical defence—horn or claw or fang —but time was not on their side. They had to adapt what was ready to hand: brains well above average and delicate palms and fingers.

They used their wits, and here we are a million or so years later able to meditate upon the achievement. The brain grew, and thanks to stick and stone and strong social ties, the awful danger passed. It passed and reoccurred. For while our ancestors were pursuing their extraordinary adventure, the climate was playing equally extraordinary tricks; tricks which have no parallel in terrestrial meteorology.

During the last million years or so—the dates are in dispute —the earth has been subjected to periodic glaciations. There have been four. We are slowly recovering from the last. A series of this sort is without precedent in planetary history. During these periods of extreme cold, the polar ice-caps thicken and spread, and perpetual mountain snows descend, century by century, into the surrounding valleys; the earth's ocean reservoirs recede as the waters accumulate locked up, frozen at the poles and in the mountains. Shore lines are extended—to be subsequently flooded during interglaciations —and arctic conditions spread throughout what are now temperate areas, and temperate conditions over what are now tropical ones.

The primate is a hot-weather animal. Our distant and still arboreal cousins in South America, Africa and Southern Asia bear witness. Africa, our ancestral cradle, was deeply involved in those successive waves of hot and cold, dry and wet—and so of forest, savannah and desert.

The primate struggle to survive was never allowed a respite or a breathing space. There was a recurring challenge, and therefore the need for a recurring response. Every victory was a preparation for the next onslaught. The power to adapt was the criterion of survival. The brain, whose extravagant growth is a biological phenomenon, was never given an opportunity to be content with its size or its complexity. It was urged on from without.

Unfavourable climatic conditions reduce to a fragment or wipe out whole species which, because of their specializations, are adapted to and prisoners of an environment. They have staked their all on the *status quo*, but permanence is always illusory. Man escaped from the prison of specialization and used this miraculous new thing—the brain.

What is a brain?

The brain is not a modern invention. It came into being long ago in answer to an antique problem—intercellular communication. The problem is recurrent on all levels of biological and social organization. Stated briefly it is this: when organic units combine they need to be able to send and receive messages, messages nutritive and informative, messages chemical and electric. This is true of the cells in a body; of branches of industry, commerce or departments of government. The problem is solved in different ways according to the size, the structure and the nature of the undertaking.

Biologically, communication and control were evolved in three fairly distinct stages, each stage arose in response to the growth in size and complexity of the organism.

The problem has an obvious solution when the units to be linked are few in number. For example three cells need only six lines or nerves, but ten cells need ninety. It is not difficult to see the impractability of this ideally simple linkage when the cellular strength of an organism runs into millions, which is the case with even small insects.

About 500 million years ago larger organisms are found to have scrapped the nerve net in favour of one or more nerve knots or ganglia.

This system robs the cell of its total individuality, and substitutes for it a step on the road to socialism: a system of delegation and division, of local or regional headquarters— knots. This plan is still *de rigueur* among the insects, for example, and is highly efficient for such small fry.

This solution is, however, much too sprawling and decentralized for larger forms of life, and approximately 350 million years ago—with, it seems the lamprey—the brain put in its first tenative appearance.

The spinal cord with a bulge at one end—budding brain— became the prototype for all go-ahead animals. An autocrat arose in the head.

Along the main line of evolution direct representation— village democracy by a show of hands—was replaced first by the ganglia system—delegated regional representation—and then by spinal cord and brain—central government.

By almost any standard 350 million years is a long time and indicates that the brain neither had its head turned by success nor employed its monopoly to create a tyranny. It was excessively moderate; absurdly moderate. It was the switchboard and the operator at the control centre of a system of communication and yet it behaved as though it were blind to its own potential. It had not come into being in order to dominate but to help out. It solved a problem, rose to the occasion, had its day and, like a faithful servant, sank back into anatomical anonymity. The result was that, as a rule, the larger the animal the smaller the percentage of brain to body.

From the invention of the brain until quite recently, evolution took its patient course experimenting on land, at sea and in the air, as though nothing of particular note had happened, with limbs and fins and wings and things. Even a mere million years ago an intelligent observer (such as you

or me—if we could have been there), would, in all probability, have predicted that the brain—a limited solution, a
mechanism, like the heart or the liver—had no future.

The adaptation of the forelimbs for handling gave the lie
to this imaginary prediction. The primates paved the way for
an evolutionary breakthrough by learning to squat on their
hind legs and to turn things over, to throw and drop and aim
with arm and hand set free. Simian palms and nails are
delicate things by jungle standards, they provide grasp and
feel in places and situations where falls are far and fatal.

The growth and elaboration of the brain ran parallel with
these structural adjustments, and there is no reason to assume
an upper limit to cerebral extension. The brain has this additional peculiarity: no other internal or external organ of the
body can grow indefinitely without causing considerable
embarrassment to its owner. The rocks are littered with the
fossils of species who knew, in some way or another, no
moderation. Nothing has ever died of a surfeit of intelligence.

The ape's brain is constructed on exactly the same prin-
ciples as man's; it is rather smaller but the great difference lies
not in size but complexity. The large human brain is not of
very recent origin. It can be compared to a plot of land which
was long since requisitioned, forgotten about and then suddenly developed. It is precisely because of this complexity that
detailed study of the brain is absolutely necessary and, of
course, almost impossible. For it is a cardinal principle of
science that it is necessary to isolate in order to analyse, and
the brain does not lend itself to this sort of treatment.
Because of the difficulty of breaking down mental processes
into their constituent parts we know very little, but that little
is worth the telling.

Despite the special character of the brain, there is apparently nothing special about the 10,000 million cells of

which an average human brain is made up; for cells trans-
planted into the brain from elsewhere in the body are perfectly well able to adapt themselves to their new milieu.
Moreover, the brain is self-powered—as are other parts of
the body—that is to say that the electrical charges that activate
the brain arise in it; there is no external source of energy.

Although the brain, vis-à-vis the rest of the nervous
system, appears to be highly centralized, within itself it is
regionalized. Comparative anatomy reveals that, in evolution, the development of certain regions of the brain is
paralleled by the development of specific behaviour. Thus
sight, hearing, speech and perceptual discrimination, for
example, are associated with specific areas.

The office of the brain, which is an extension of the nervous
system, was primarily sensual, but it has enlarged its province
in a particular direction, and it is with this enlargement—the
frontal lobe—that man is most directly concerned. For,
although the frontal lobe exists in all mammals, its enormous
prominence in man inevitably suggests that it holds the clue
to human achievement. In animals the forebrain is responsible
for bringing past experience to bear on the solution of present
problems. In man it extends this responsibility to cover,
among other things, the integration of personality—the
integration of all the centres of the brain—deliberation, as
opposed to spontaneity, and conceptual thinking. The source
of man's power seems to lie there; in a protrusion above the
eyes.

The archives of the brain are not housed in the forebrain,
they are regionalized—distributed throughout the centres in
which they arise—but the forebrain acts as a co-ordinator of
these memories and so provides what we recognize as associations. Thus, the availability of past experience is not a
specific function, but a series of them. A memory can be

evoked singly or a group may be evoked simultaneously. The parts contribute to the whole and the efficient association of past experiences is one of our main criteria of intellectual and artistic value. The linkage must be extremely delicate as it is certainly of recent origin, being still a faculty almost totally absent in some people and highly developed in others. It is worth noting that the mental disease of dissociation is explicable in these terms; for if the associative area of the brain, which gives coherence to the individual personality, breaks down, the unity of the mind is shattered. Memories that are not co-ordinated function as fragments and individuality is split into a multiplicity.

We have reached manhood now with a vengeance, so it may be profitable to retrace our steps slightly in order to remind ourselves of his distinctive scent. In a few pages we have jumped from the brain of the lamprey 350 million years ago to the brain we recognize as our own. The excuse for so cavalier a treatment of so vast a stretch of time is the absence of anything cerebrally worthy of recording that occurred in it. The size of the brain and its complexity crept up or was static during all that time. The brain was, as it were, an average or backward child, who suddenly blossomed into genius in middle age, and exploded into dominance in a flash a million or less years ago. We are trying to explain so magnificent and so retarded a florescence. It may not have happened thus. We may never know for sure.

As is to be expected, there are no hard and fast lines to be drawn or found between the brain of an ape and the brain of a man; nor for that matter between brains at all, anywhere or at any time. Animals are not, as was once popularly and naively believed, activated by a battery of instincts: of reflex actions, pieces of more than usually delicate machinery with built-in, automatic responses. Reflex actions, in fact, play an insignificant part in the behaviour of all higher animals who are activated by nervous mechanisms which display themselves as moods, and which are primed and released at various levels.

The brain of man extended and elaborated all its parts with marked emphasis on the forebrain. In terms of solid gain, this provided an area concerned with the association of memories, forethought and controls; all of which gave time to check impulse and allow man, by a process of deliberation, to consider the consequences of an action before taking or rejecting it.

These are uniquely human achievements, for the chimpanzee's brain—which is the next biggest star in the cerebral firmament—does not possess the qualities necessary to enable its owner to hold an image long enough to reflect on it. The limitations which such a brain imposes are excruciating even to contemplate. Armed mentally thus the chimpanzee can admittedly respond with great aplomb to a given situation, *when it arises*, but is totally incapable of making any sort of provision for the possibility of its reoccurrence or of providing for a contingency. These limitations render the mental rehearsal of a series of possible responses to a situation out of the question. There is therefore no conceptual thinking, no planning and no control of feeling apart from that induced by the exigencies of the immediate circumstances; thus appetite may be overwhelmed by fear, or fear by social responsibility. Control of this kind is subjective. Self-control on a human level, in its highest form, is objective; and control of the self is an absolute prerequisite for control of the environment. In order to gain control it is necessary to diagnose and to understand; violence is fast and ineffective.

This chapter, entitled mind, begins with a discussion of the brain. The reason for this is of course obvious: the mere existence of the brain and the most rudimentary knowledge of its functioning reveal the necessity for a word to summarize the results it produces. All that is implied by the words 'mind' and 'mentality' is unthinkable without there being a tangible structure with which to associate it.[1]

The brain clearly specializes in mind; but it is not proven that the brain has a monopoly of it. No one would quarrel with so bald a statement now, but it has not always been so.

There is of course nothing tangible about the mind: it is a function, not an entity, and for this reason the word 'mentality' is often preferred. The words 'soul' and 'spirit' are poetic or pseudo-religious abstractions and are meaningless when introduced into rational argument. Mind is suspect as a word too, because of the tendency to attribute to it a concrete existence. It is used here because in current use it refers to the totality of mental processes, and because it has subtle overtones that the word 'mentality' has not.

It seems reasonable to begin an analysis of mind by regarding it as a function. There is nothing remotely revolutionary about this definition, but it cannot be repeated too often, since the whole subject which is difficult enough anyway, has been overlaid with millennial accretions of prejudice. The growth of individual consciousness has, in addition, led to personal mental secrecy or chastity—the mind seems to resent being undressed publicly or even privately.

Mind, then, regarded as a function, is excused the necessity of being visible or tangible or occupying space. Mind is to an organism what speed is to a car. In the latter case a driver knows that the engine is the seat of power, he also knows that the engine, the cooling-system, the streamlining, etc., contribute in different ways to the speed at which his car moves; but it would be a mad mechanic, who took his car to pieces in order to find the speed. Speed, however fast or slow, is the function of a car as mind is the function of a body.

What sort of function is mind then? Mind is the function of learning. Can it be defined by listing all those things of necessity attributed to it—reason, will, reflection, intelligence, intellect, perceptual and conceptual thinking, association of ideas, foresight, curiosity, purposefulness, self-control, conscience, sense of humour, artistic creativity and appreciation? Mind is any one of these things or combination of them. What runs through all these functions and gives the list coherence? One thing only, perhaps. Each of these attributes requires for its proper functioning the concentrated efforts of the parts. The unity of the parts creates the whole, and that unity, as always, creates an entirely new thing—mind; something unsuspected in the parts, unsuspected but evidently latent.

This is what we find throughout the whole of nature. This is the pattern of evolution: firstly, free particles condensing into atoms, atoms which differ among themselves according to the quantity and arrangements of the particles they contain. Secondly, atoms condensing into molecules which differ among themselves according to the quantity and arrangement of the atoms they contain. And each new combination of particles or atoms creating, in uniting, qualities which could not be predicted from an analysis of the parts that combined in the making of it. That is the beginning and the end of what is conveniently referred to as inorganic matter.

The inorganic is followed by the organic whose classifications and frontiers are also blurred. Molecules condense into patterns and form cells. Cells condense into patterns until the surface of the Planet kindles and then blazes into life; until the whole of nature is there before our eyes—our eyes that are part of it. And what is it all? Matter, particles, energy uniting in slow time.

And mind? Where, at what stage, does mind come in; how far down this burgeoning tree of matter?

Sherrington, who was quoted at the beginning of this chapter, writes:

> But if there be no essential difference between life and all the rest. What becomes of the difference between mind and no-mind? There is that to be answered. To answer we may follow the hierarchy of systems and things downwards and see at what point mind quits it. Unless we can do that who knows that mind has left it? Of ourselves, yes, we know we have a mind. And the dragonfly? Yes, it may have a mind. And amoeba? It may have but how are we to know? What of the grey rock? Do we know? If the imagined boundary between life and no-life will not stand examination, may it not be that that between mind and no-mind will have to go?[2]

We are like dogs on a scent, which we follow and follow and follow, running at first because the scent is strong, but as it gets fainter and fainter dropping into a trot, then into a walk until finally we are at a standstill, sniffing in all directions where the scent gives out— but did the scent give out? Its apparent absence could be attributed to the inefficiency of our noses.

Is not the only possible explanation of this incessant and exasperating trailing away of what we believed to be clear-cut distinctions due to the prejudice of our viewpoint, our eyes and our language? Once evolution is accepted as a total concept and not merely intellectually, then the blurred frontier is precisely the most natural thing in the world to expect. All boundaries are illusions; evolution must create in our minds the acceptance of a world order of energy classified, purely for a probably ephemeral purpose of convenience, into tigers and moths and jerricans and marble-topped tables.

Mind is latent in all matter, and matter being energy, that is what mind is too. Energy, however, is unitary and it is in condensation that it discloses its potentialities. All condensations are patterns of energy manifesting unpredictable qualities which are latent until those patterns appear. Mind has a past which has left traces in places where the troubling intensity of life is no more, so that one can recognize that mind has passed by that way like a candle burning in an empty room. Mind is the moving frontier of evolution, leaving conquered and settled country in its wake. And we, who come after, do not see the scars of conflict or recognize the epic struggle of the worm. Mind has a past and presumably a future. From that future, mind will look back on this present. Will it recognize that we had mind? Or will it question ours as we question the eel's and the oyster's?

This is no academic argument; the point in pursuing mind down beyond recognizability to its origins is twofold. Firstly, to make quite sure that its source is understood, and obliterate any lingering suspicion that mind was introduced from outer space by olympian fiat. Secondly, to draw the now well-established deduction from this, that human nature has deep roots in a pre-human past.

The fact that man's mind is of common origin with all life does not detract in any way from its exceptional character. As has already been suggested often enough, it seems more commendable to rise than to fall. It also seems to be more optimistic to believe that to rise, not to fall, is the trend.

Having tried to put some sort of order into the mind's remote origins, it is possible to shorten our perspective and play the spotlight on ourselves.

As we have seen, man's brain is not only the largest thing of its kind on earth, it is far and away the most elaborate. This elaboration and enlargement is characterized by the growth of the forebrain and reduction of the olfactory centre, the extension of the occipital centre and the region of speech. These changes have given us a reduced sense of smell, better vision and colour sense, speech and, with a power undreamed of in the pre-human brain, conceptual thought—the real clue to man's dominance.

Because conceptual thought comes so naturally to us, it needs an effort of the imagination to conceive of mind without it, or even to conceive what other form of thinking there is on which it has been superimposed. Perceptual thinking is the response to a perceived situation: the response to a present, visible, smellable, hearable, etc., impulse. The response begins and ends with the impulse; the experience may, however, be stored, learned and realized.

Conceptual thought, on the other hand, is independent of sensual impulse. Problems, situations, possibilities are envisaged, whether or not they have been experienced, and contingent solutions are sought. This faculty is based on two extensions of the mind: firstly, the ability to consider objects or ideas as members of a class—to recognize identity and similarity; and secondly, the ability to turn over in the mind alternative courses of action or lines of thought to test them and their consequences without performing them and so, after deliberation, to take action.

Perceptual and conceptual thought are not of course mutually exclusive. They can operate separately or in conjunction, although probably not simultaneously. For example: in the solution of practical problems conceptual thought is normally employed to reduce experimentation to the minimum; a point is then sometimes reached when, floored by the complications, the mind is forced to apply the concept in order perceptually to resolve the problem. Some ideas do not lend themselves to this treatment: the concept may be too remote from the consequences of its application, in which case the ideas are submitted to the mind as data is fed into a computer, and the brain—all its parts contributing —after sufficient or insufficient concentration taps out an objective or subjective answer.

So far no mention has been made of speech. Frequently over these pages it has cried out for recognition, yet until now its claims have been deliberately side-stepped. The fact is that it plays so diverse a role socially and intellectually that it fits conveniently into no category. It shares with art a fatal distinction; merely to touch upon them is grossly to under- value them, fully to deal with them involves so long a paren- thesis that the thread of the argument of the entire book is lost.

It is difficult to know to how great an extent mind is dependent on speech for conceptual thought. Maybe speech fathered it and is fathering it still. The earliest hominoid skulls of half a million years ago are marked by swellings of the brain in the speech regions. The extreme antiquity of lan- guage is further collaborated by the extraordinary divergence of tongues among primitive peoples. The aborigines of Australia, for example, who are a mere 200,000 in number, have 500 languages to their credit.

Speech is not pre-human. The cries and grunts and songs and chatterings of animals are expressions of mood which are caught up or not by their hearers. No doubt these simple expressions of mood evolved and became a means of com- munication, and speech undoubtedly has its origins in them. Their value being unquestionable, the variety of expressions multiplied; mood launched noises on their way to language.

A great deal of human language is still a formulation of of mood. The infant recapitulates in many ways the growth of language, although this is difficult to trace owing to the rapid amalgamation of mood and imitation.

Speech plays, of course, a dual role: it is a means of communication and an aid to thought. Words are verbal signs naming objects, actions and functions; adding intensity, description and conjunction. It is impossible to say whether conceptual thought produced a language in which to clothe itself, or whether language evolved first and provided the symbols needed for the origins of conceptual thought.

When we question our own minds they do not easily yield up the secret of their processes; they give no clue at all to the origin of thought. Moreover, although human brains differ insignificantly in volume, they vary enormously in quality and in method. In addition the speed of thought is so great that it cannot be broken down into its components: words, images, associations, etc. In the absence of evidence to the contrary it seems natural to assume that the growth of language and conceptual thinking ran parallel and that they still do. For, in the first instance, it is necessary to recognize an object and give it a name. The names—to exercise an essential economy of words—must apply not only to the objects originally named but also to all other objects sufficiently resembling them in certain essential features. Words, consequently, compel the mind to classify nature. And classification is the basic imperative of conceptual thought.

It is a mistake to regard evolution as the development or improvement of isolated parts or functions. Brain and body are too highly co-ordinated not to interact. Every development of the brain must have been accompanied by overall physical adjustments however slight.

It is a misfortune that speech, which is one of the most

important achievements of man, leaves no fossil-traces of its growth. Small bulges in the speech region of the skull give an indication of size but no clue to complexity, and it is complexity that matters. So that whether we examine the brain as a whole or in parts, all we can say of a skull is that its measurements reveal certain capacities. And capacities are potentialities not actualities. The rooms in the house of the brain were sparsely, and are still inadequately furnished.

We do not lack evidence so miserably in every field of study of our past. Certain activities leave traces, and it is for that reason that tool- and weapon-making appear to have received an undue share of attention. But our attention can only be given to what is available for examination. Moreover, the interest lies less in the tools themselves than in the state of mental development that they reveal in those who fashioned them. So it is that in the absence of direct evidence of mental evolution we turn to its material manifestations.

We are like detectives who in their efforts to reconstruct a situation are limited by the total availability of the evidence. What is constructed of durable materials survives, but durability is a relative term. Flints can be so mishandled by weathering and friction that it often cannot confidently be stated whether they have been fashioned by man or by nature. Thus primitive weapons are not distinguishable from naturally shaped flints and vice versa. In addition, long before weapons were made they were used as found, if of convenient shape and size. These latter are lost, of course, as evidence; the primitively chipped tool is always suspect, and it is only later, and how much later it is hard to tell, when craftsmanship has attained a certain refinement, that evidence is valid and doubt gives place to certainty. The truly transitional stage is lost and goes unrecorded.

The difficulties do not end there, for the likelihood of

finding weapons of definite manufacture is dependent upon a multitude of factors—the exposure of the strata in which they fell or were buried, the shifting of strata through earthquakes, mountain building, development of faults and other geological upheavals, their burial in surface sediments from rivers and glaciers, the nearness of prehistoric sites to present centres of civilization, the rise and fall of oceans with the consequent recession and advance of shore-lines, caused by the release and locking-up of water by polar and mountain glaciation.

Thus the archaeologist sacks the world to unearth the prehistory of man, and what does he find—when he finds anything? Bones and stones, the ashes of his fires and, in a few instances, drawings, paintings, scratches on the walls of the caves which were his home. The bones are human or of animals, his victims, brought back from the hunt to the cave or clearing, cooked or uncooked to be eaten. The bones of his victims and the stones he has chipped were the tools of his trade, and the weapons of his attack. He was an industrious carnivore and sometimes cannibal.

But it is not the tool or the weapon itself that rivets the attention, nor the flake or core, the handaxe, harpoon or needle. It is the clue that each is to the understanding of the state of mind of the maker. It is not *what* they made that counts so much; it is *that* they made anything at all. They are the first things consciously designed on this Planet. They date the departure of mind off on that fantastic venture which we are still pursuing. It is as though many thousands of years hence Grand Central Station were excavated. The archaeologists engaged on the undertaking would, no doubt, discover that towards the end of the second millennium A.D., man was still living in a Railway Age. Now it seems unlikely that it would interest science at that time to re-discover how engines were made or signal-boxes put together; the point of the excavations would be to reveal the stage of civilization reached at this and that point in history.

During the last 500,000 years the physical evolution of man has been virtually at a standstill. Half a million years is not a long time by evolutionary standards, but since during it there has been staged perhaps the whole of the human story it is of vital interest to us to recapitulate it in the utmost detail. The story is pieced together over this period, less and less from fossil bones and more and more from what man made and how he made it. Tools reveal man's way of living, weapons his ways of killing. His activities reveal the evolution of his mind, and the evolution of his mind is the clue to his culture, his civilization, and the level of his thought.

History began some 7,000 years ago with the earliest known written records. 7,000 years is one per cent of the human story, for the other ninety-nine per cent we depend upon unwritten sources. That unit— one per cent— emphasizes the prodigious speeding up of mental evolution from the first chipped words, the hieroglyphs and pictograms; the sowing of the first corn, the domesticating of animals, the wooden hoe, the flint sickle, the earthenware pot and perhaps the wheel.

Half a million years ago the whole emphasis and pattern of life altered. Biological evolution, as it had proceeded for million years after million years with natural selection as its censor, tapered to an end, and a new era began. The brain swung into prominence and the Planet would never be the same again.

It is necessary at this stage of the argument to retrace our steps a little in order to pick up a thread which is apt to be disregarded because it is so tangled in the skein of mind.

So far in this chapter mind has been referred to and studied as a manifold of individual entities, the separate and isolated functions of individual brains. It is natural to approach the problem of mind in this way because the brain, which seems to be the key to the mind, is a tangible conglomeration of cells locked up in the individual animal head; this leads us, inevitably, to the conclusion that mind is an individual thing too, and its intangibility does nothing to subtract from it its intensely personal nature.

However, it is worth considering whether this attitude of ours, this view of mind as fragmental and egotistic, is not a prejudice.

There is in fact a great deal of evidence to support the alternative theory: that mind is not confined to the brain and body with which it is associated. It must always be realized that our ways of thinking are steeped in the conventions of society and that consequently our observations project into any object under study something of ourselves, the observers. To educate ourselves to observe objectively requires discipline and training. There may even be situations which do not permit one to see without disturbing the thing seen. It is a stealthy business.

A stage has been reached in this book when we shall be thinking solely in terms of human mind; mind in man, mind in history, mind in society, and hence the play of mind over civilization and religion. It is therefore an appropriate moment to put forward a theory of mind and of mental activity so that it may be tested against the events we are about to relate. It warns the reader also to be on his guard against bias in the writer. The idea is tentative and makes no claim to being more than a line of approach.

The individual members of any species living in groups would clearly be favoured in the struggle for existence if they possessed a compass of vocal expression which served as a means of communication. There would be no need, at first, for any great range of expression. The extent of the need would obviously depend upon the mental level reached.

There are clearly many ways of communicating without the use of the sophistications to which man is accustomed. Communication can be by the distinctive noise, roar, neigh, bark, howl, song, etc., with which we are all familiar; but apart from these there are many others—the exuding of scent through the pores, ruffled feathers, colour change, posture, bristling, arching of back, pricking of ears, thrust of the head, etc.; there would seem to be almost no part of the body that cannot contribute its quota to the range of communication. All the above expressions are indications of mood. There is, so far as we know, no intent to communicate warning, threat, submission, sexual preparedness, etc. Expression of mood has, however, that result. Friend or foe is alerted to the situation and makes its appropriate response. In other words, the mood of an animal induces a mood which will be in sympathy with or antagonistic to its own. Expression of mood does, therefore, serve as a means of communication. This is the first point in the argument.

There is every reason to believe that these means of communication are universal among at least the higher animals. They are diverse and extremely subtle, but some are no more than symbols recognizable and interpretable between individuals. Apart from and in addition to them are the expressions of group mood: the moods of gregarious animals, such as migrations, the wheeling of a flock of birds, the wind of fear running through the herd, the thrill of expectation that strikes alarm or shocks into action. There is such a thing as group response. How are moods communicated through a group? Is there such a thing as group consciousness—or *was* there such a thing? If this is or were so, then the mind first appeared as a group phenomenon based, it is true, on the individual brain but spread undifferentiated over the species.

Must it not then follow that man inherited and shared this original form of communication and group behaviour?

Man, it seems, has always been a speaking animal and has therefore always supplemented his gestures and his physical expressions of mood by speech. The spoken word has its limitations in primitive life; it is noisy and therefore liable to be dangerous; it is excellent for short-range communication only. Study of contemporary primitive societies reveals the existence of group impulse, action and response.

This, then, is the second point in the argument: is it not possible that the coming of speech did not at first supplant group mood? Is it possible that primitive bands depended largely upon the interaction of mind between their members? If so this stage of human evolution can be called pre-individualistic. Our own intense individualism makes it difficult for us to imagine—makes us incredulous of—anything resembling group consciousness. Our minds are likely to reject out of hand an idea so foreign and so hostile to them. Can we, without prejudice, accept the possibility of there having once existed a stage of mental evolution when mind was integrated within groupings? Can we, the painfully and aggressively disintegrated individualists do this?

In the next chapters an attempt will be made to provide a certain amount of illustrative detail. It is only possible to say now in general terms that such ideas as the visiting of the sins of parents on the children; punishment of the individual by the destruction of himself, his possessions and his family; blood feuds; immolation of wife, or family slaves and servants on the death of the husband or head, are barbarous in our eyes because as individuals we think of death, crime and punishment as phenomena which relate exclusively to the individual. Our limited knowledge of tribal law reinforces this theory. In many cases no legal provision was made for the possibility of the murder of kinsman by kinsman. The only way to account for there being no such law is to assume that there was no such crime. Kin could only suffer and rejoice together, and punishment could not — was never — meted out to the individual. The group had no law, no need of any law, which inflicted punishment on a part of its integrated self.

If we accept this line of argument, or even do no more than allow that it may be fertile, then we have reached this stage: until comparatively recently, until— may we hazard a date?— 7,000 years ago, at the beginning of history, mind was less an individual than a group phenomenon; and family, troop and herd and all groupings from man downwards acted and thought— within their limitations— socially as entities comprising a few or many parts.

Could it be that self-consciousness: individualism, was not— or was scarcely— known until then? Is not the Old Testament myth of Eve and the serpent the sort of dramatized record that one would expect to survive of a prehistoric occurrence— the beginning of self-consciousness, when man looked inwards and became aware of himself? By the same token the myth of Cain and Abel may record the disintegration of social ties when kin murdered kin because mind was changing its focus: the parts no longer in harmony, the group fragments.

The process must have been slow and long; it is undoubtedly still going on. We tend to measure the pace of history by the speed of its advance guard. But societies hand on the torch from one to the other and drop back; some take no part in the race, others are far behind.

Self-consciousness, if one can detach oneself from one's own, has the appearance of a mental development which has evolved from a pre-individualistic state. If self-consciousness is subtracted from the attributes of mind, what is the residue from which it arose? Mind evolving from its small beginnings was shared and then, enlarging, spreading, sought new outlets until eventually in the course of its inquiries reflected and began to wonder about itself. It analysed, and the synthesis fell apart.

Mind evolves. Recently it has been evolving at a grotesque speed. The recipients of its latest convulsions are inevitably revolutionaries. Is there any possibility of reconstructing that slow passage of mind, and of following it as it gathered speed, or of reconstructing the passage from group to individual, when here and there a man stood out and questioned tradition, who felt that he was different; who was ashamed of it; who hid his new knowledge or flaunted it; who was feared and admired because he was different or who was scorned or hated for it?

Does anthropology, does history give any warrant for holding this view? Does the evolution of mind in these terms form a framework within which historical facts add up to an historical theory? We shall confront these problems in the next chapters, and along with them an extension of this tentative theory—namely, if group-consciousness yields to self-consciousness, what next? The mind is restless; self-consciousness can be no more than a step or two along the road of man's immense journey.

10 Mind, Prehistoric

. . the thinking brain has turned eagerly to the first possible glimpses of itself. The millennial period of its unconscious evolution ends before the mirror; a new phase begins.

W. Grey Walter, *The Living Brain*

AS PHYSICAL EVOLUTION reaches the end of its course it tapers off, busies itself with refinements, puts final touches with slight, quick strokes of an intuitive brush and turns to its next canvas. Psychological evolution, until then an idea in the back of the mind, now comes into focus and all the forces of creation will be concentrated in this new direction.

From now on understanding of the past must be sought in the interpretation of the more and more complicated and more extensive states of mind that manifest themselves increasingly as we approach the present moment. The study of man, properly speaking, is the study of the evolution of consciousness—a statement which is surely verging on the obvious, Yet it is the failure to view history in this light that deprives it of the sense and meaning which we expect or hope it will yield. It is necessary to shed most of our conceptions, pre-conceptions and sophistications, and to enter the past unmolested by our superior moral standards, our prejudices and—most of all perhaps—by our deplorably provincial measures of time.

In the next three chapters an attempt will be made to sketch the outline of man's immediate prehistory, ancient history and modern history, in terms of his fluctuating but increasing consciousness. Man is still a young animal, but time enough has flowed since he first haltingly trod the earth for his trends certainly, and his destiny probably, to be discernible.

History began a mere six thousand years ago with the first few written records of which we have knowledge. At which time the civilizations of the great river valleys—Nile, Tigris–Euphrates, Indus and Yellow River—had probably already been in existence for a thousand years. It is mainly on the excavations of varying extent made in these four areas that we are dependent for our reconstruction of the first 2,500 years of ancient history, that is to say, up to the beginning of the Iron Age.

Those four river valleys nourished the only civilizations that were on the main stream of evolutionary advance. For this reason and for the sake of brevity their contemporaries elsewhere are ignored here—reluctantly because comparative study is rewarding.

When we attempt, however, as we are attempting in this chapter, to probe behind civilization, and to understand the nature of man and society antecedent to history, we have no such sources of information. It is for that reason that we turn to the study of primitive societies which remained until recently or still remain untouched by civilization, and assume with certain reservations that from such similar societies sprang historical man.

Partly because of these very dissimilar sources of information, it is exceedingly difficult to bridge the gulf between primitive societies and the great riverine civilizations of the Ancient World to which they must have given birth. When civilization begins it seems to begin with a bang. Archaeologists digging in the most ancient places find that as they descend through the successive layers of continuously occupied and therefore continuously being re-built sites, that there has been, as is to be expected, an evolution of techniques and inventions. But the lowest levels reveal the existence of peoples who had attained a high degree of civilization. Who were they? From where did they come? Possibly all these civilizations sprang from a common origin: successive migrations down the great river valleys from the Euro-Asiatic steppes, or from North and East Africa sweeping eastwards. The only alternative is to postulate that there was a spontaneous dilation of consciousness which occurred successively amongst widely dispersed peoples. The discoveries that they made were in any case identical: agriculture, domestication of animals, pottery and weaving.

It was the development of alluvial-valley agriculture, and so of a method of producing large surpluses of food, which made the revolution and drew the line between tribal society and civilization. The distinction is vital and it is no exaggeration to claim that the whole of history—the sum of the evolution of mankind since that discovery—rests solidly on the basis of it. This point will be discussed more fully in the next chapter. Here it is our task to pry into the mind of man antecedent to, and poised unknowingly on the brink of civilization.

Light is thrown on pre-civilization mind mainly from three totally different sources: from Stone Age excavations, from societies which still exist or which existed until recently in the remote and backward parts of the world, and from a study of animal, particularly primate behaviour in captivity and in the wild. The former are few in number, and what they have so far revealed to us is insignificant by comparison with what living societies of primitive peoples can be made, by patient understanding and sensitive inquiry, to yield.

Prior to the practice of agriculture, man lived as an animal off the land to which he contributed nothing in return except his excreta, his urine and his dead self. Men were hunters and wanderers, living tribally in defined territories. Each territory was of such a size as to ensure in normal times a sufficiency of food for the particular group. But times are not usually normal so that populations must have varied violently—as animal populations still do—in bad years being reduced drastically, or being wiped out completely and then, on the other hand, over long, favourable periods increasing beyond the capacity of the territory to support them: hence territorial violations and inter-tribal war. Apart from these variations there were of course the vaster long-term fluctuations of heat and cold which caused wholesale migrations following in the wake of animal migrations: the source of their food and their quarry. Man was driven hither and thither at the behest of his stomach. Economically the case of primitive men and wild animals is not dissimilar. Both depend upon a bounteous supply of food being available, without having the means to grow or rear or conserve it.

However, man had certain distinctions, and it is the evolution of these that must be analysed and pursued. His ability to make tools and weapons, and the conceptual powers that their making exacted has already been discussed. In addition he was an artist and the significance and interpretation of his art will reoccur throughout the following pages. But the greatest problem he had to face was a social one, and upon the resolution of this depended all else—it still does.

At first it seems likely that men lived in bands; if this is so one can imagine them distributed sparsely over wide territories. Bands would therefore be relatively isolated and each would merely and barely maintain itself in its prescribed ecological setting. The band would be promiscuous and at this stage consciousness largely collective. The band would share learned experience and live and hunt as a team.

Evolution can get stuck at this stage as we know from our

study of contemporary primitive societies. Those bands, however, which were successful due to improved hunting techniques, or a change of diet in the direction of higher protein intake, or natural increase in available food supply, would grow in size. But there is obviously an optimum size for a hunting band, and wherever this size was exceeded through successful adaptation a critical point would be reached at which the band would split analogous to cell division. Now as long as the bands so formed separated, became autonomous and lost contact with each other, social evolution would be at a standstill. Men simply became more numerous because they had learnt to exploit the environment to greater advantage. But social evolution can halt again at this stage—as it has done with the primates.

If, however, bands that split up separate but do not isolate themselves from each other entirely, some sort of loose relationship is created between them by, for example, the interchange of women. In this way conflict between the bands is reduced if not eliminated, and further evolution becomes possible. Drawing an analogy again from biology: cells combine and a multi-cellular organism is built up.

From this point on it becomes a matter of the degree of unity achieved. The bands are parts of the tribe, all of whose members will in the course of time be more or less related to each other. This can be thought of as a sort of extended kinship group.

Man had to learn to live with his own kind in ever larger communities. He had to acquire an enforceable social tradition. He had to achieve a self-control that would enable him to subject himself, when the need arose, to a greater necessity: the survival of the community. Co-operation, as always, not aggressive self-interest, was the key to further evolution. The tribe—the pre-civilization unit—devised a system of taboos. These taboos constituted the morality of the tribe. Evolution depended on the one hand upon the ability to submit to the taboos, and on the other the ability to evolve them. The community would flourish because of them, and its members in spite of them. The balance was delicate; the chances of success slight.

Nothing is more revealing of the nature of man than the politico-social organization to which he is subject and to which he subscribes. At this point it is necessary to make a very wide and not very controversial generalization: almost without exception all primitive societies rest on a foundation of kinship. The tie of kinship is stronger than, and has been grafted on to the tie of family. A kin is normally a group of people occupying a defined territory, who are so closely bound together that they hold their lives in common. An offence or an affront against one is an offence or affront against all—hence the feud. Solidarity within, animosity without; strife is pushed radically out to the frontier. Aggressiveness must not find a civil outlet. The survival of the fittest means the survival of those who are able to sink their differences within the sanction of a taboo, and to vent their wrath across the frontier, not within it.

It seems very probable then, that promiscuity preceded individual marriage. If so, then the primitive band practises an extreme of communism, living as a unit and holding all in common: suffering and rejoicing as one, eating in communion, taking all decisions jointly in council. There is nothing fanciful about this picture. There was no Golden Age of the Noble Savage. This seemingly ideal socio-political organization only obtained within the band. This is a pre-individualistic state of evolution. Man was not yet self-conscious. His speculations were superficial. He was not *aware* of the organization he had contrived; aware of it as an experiment. Neither his life span nor his mind provided him with the vision to regard his situation as anything but fixed and eternal. His group solidarity obliged him to transfer his hostility over the border, and made his neighbours pay the cost to him of his repressed domestic animal spirits. So whenever bands increased in number, began practising exogamy and achieved thereby a measure first of tolerance of each other and then of unity, kinship groups were formed and inter-tribal war became the price to pay for civil peace. If war there had to be, it was a fair price to pay.

In such circumstances a man was protected—apart from the hazards of inter-tribal feud and war—by his kinsmen and his membership of a kin. The mind of the individual and the mind of the tribe were indivisible.[1] Kin acted together and thought alike, and the system was not questioned by the individual members, who did not in any case distinguish themselves from the group. Kinship depended for its survival upon a certain level of consciousness. It would begin to break up as soon as the first few men turned their gaze inwards and became aware of their individuality: became competitive, assertive, ambitious, speculative; became self-conscious. When this began to happen, that is to say, when the aperture of consciousness began to open, it affected an individual here and there like a mutation, casually and at random. It must have brought about very gradually a change in two specific directions: in command, and in the attitude towards possession.

Kinship had to adjust itself to a new situation. Individualism, which we take for granted, and self-interest, which we accept as the criterion by which most men form their judgments, must have been a terrifying or exhilarating mental experience for those who were first affected by it. These first non-conformists inspired a variety of conflicting emotions among their kinsmen: fear, resentment, ridicule, hatred, adoration and awe.

When superior intelligence is rare, and the outlets for its talents limited, inevitably and inexorably, it captures authority. Within a tribe it would rule—wherever it was permitted to survive—by virtue of the respect or the fear it inspired. Uneasy must have lain *their* heads. The ambivalent attitude towards authority in general and kings in particular was born.

It is pertinent at this juncture to inquire into the origins of totemism, for all societies practise it or practised it prior to attaining civilization. Its origins are clouded in obscurity. Contemporary totemic societies are inevitably incapable of the necessary introspection, historical or oral tradition, or curiosity to enable them to be of much help in fathoming what is so ancient and seems to strange a phenomenon.

It would be outrageous, in view of the still conflicting theories that are current, and the vast and erudite literature on the subject, to pretend to the reader that it is possible to summarize so much research in a few words—or worse, to give the impression that an agreed solution is being presented. All that can be expressed here is an opinion derived from the argument that runs through this book.

From the start the time element cannot be over-emphasized. In speaking of totemism we are speaking in terms of sociological evolution, spread over at least some tens of thousands of years. To ignore the time-scale is fatal, since to do so makes the extraordinary ramifications and elaborations of totemism completely incomprehensible. Evolution, whether physical or social, is not a neat, clipped, rational process, but a luxuriant contortion, a fandango of antlers, centipedes and dervishes.

Secondly, it should be borne in mind that totemism was a

world-wide phenomenon common to peoples who were certainly never in communication with each other; its development must consequently have been parallel and isolated.

The first factor, time, is difficult to imagine because of its length; and nothing can therefore be done with it apart from allowing it a vague, overall control. The second factor, geographical dispersion, is difficult to understand because it indicates independent development of a similar kind. The importance from our point of view of this second factor is that it demands an explanation of a totally general kind: totemism must have arisen for very obvious reasons from a very general need.

To consider, then, the problem.

Speech is probably as old as man. Its development, that is to say, its refinement and richness of vocabulary, is recent; parallel with the phenomenal historical growth of mind. Primitive speech must have been both mainly substantive; a matter of giving names to people and things, and economic; hostile to neologisms. Men named each other individually and their neighbours collectively and the words they used would be familiar words, made to serve a dual purpose: names of animals mainly, but also of plants or natural phenomena. Sporting and scouting people still do this today, so do nations: the lion and the kangaroo, the eagle and the bear, the springbok, the dragon, the thistle and the leek—to mention but a few.

Every tribe would naturally discover in the course of time the name its neighbours gave it. Tribes were named from without. But it is a truism to say that words were deemed to have a significance, even a magical power, beyond their simple, utilitarian purposes. They were and still are often regarded not as symbols or conventional sounds, but as personifications of the things that they name. To know the

name of a thing is to be in possession to an indefinable degree
of that thing, and to be able in certain circumstances to
exercise a benign or malign power over it. Such was the
power of the word during its uniquely oral genesis; and
history abounds with examples of its persistence even up to
the present day.

People, according to this theory, called themselves what
they were called, and their name is THEM. The totem is their
name, themselves, their ancestor, their emblem and badge
and, in a sense, their god. The identification becomes complete. The totem is sacred and enjoys the same rights as the
members of the clan. To kill the totem is to kill a member of
the tribe. The clan becomes its name.

The totem is, however, on occasions slain and eaten. The
occasions are solemn and festive, as our holy holidays are. The
slaying and the feasting are restricted by custom and performed by the community as a whole. The tribe jointly
accepts the risk, the crime, the enjoyment, and all are
obliged to partake. The meal is sacrificial. The emblem, the
god, in 'holy' communion is eaten. All the members of the
tribe eat their totem which is their substance, and are rein-
forced and strengthened thereby. The feast denotes tribal
solidarity – an at-one-ment with the flesh and blood of their
totem: themselves.

If this explanation is correct, it accounts for the widespread appeal of totemism. Its origins are simple: the naming,
the mystical attribute of the word. Its value is obvious, it is
social cement. It provided exactly what was needed to bind
individuals together, and to give the kin, the clan, the tribe,
the incentive to live at peace together. It was a sure foundation
and a step which, if not taken, would have ruled out the
possibility of civilization.

What have taboos to do with totems? Only this, that round

the tribe and the tribe's totem, laws, restrictions and inhibitions cluster. Tribes are evolutionary catalysts—as city states and nations will be later on. Many of the taboos are directly connected with the complicated relationships that are built up between each tribe and its totem; these are peripheral to the argument. Exogamy—the incest taboo—is not one of them. What has totemism to do with exogamy? Nothing, except that the totem is the tribe, and the tribe must not become an incestuous unit and disintegrate.

The first signs of self-consciousness, self-assertion and egotism are suppressed. Promiscuity is only feasible within a very small community, and communities inevitably grow in size and so outgrow it. Totemism, tribal nationalism, sublimates the individual. As long as there is solidarity and all things, including the woman, are held in common, all is well, but as soon as individualism raises its head the society is threatened with disintegration. Sex is disruptive. In a primitive society there are not many things that a man *can* possess, real or personal. Property, moveable or immoveable, is almost non-existent and cannot therefore give rise to disputes over ownership. Women are an exception. All basic needs—and all needs *are* basic—physical and psychological are better satisfied when communally attempted; all, except sex. Sex is normally dual and normally private. Among incipiently self-conscious people all the advantages of communal life would be vitiated if sexual appetites and jealousies were given their head. The two universal crimes of primitive peoples are incest and murder; the two are very closely connected.

Promiscuity in a tribe, any of whose members were on the threshold of self-consciousness, would lead to that tribe's disintegration. Hence the taboo and the elaborate precautions to ensure its enforcement. We know nothing about those communities which avoided taking these precautions because they have not survived for the benefit of our study.

Finally it only remains to be noted in support of this theory, that exogamy disappears altogether or lingers on as a vague incestuous inhibition as soon as communities increase sufficiently in size to enable the law to be relaxed. The larger the community, the less vulnerable it becomes to the sexual appetites of its constituents. States and cities are not overthrown by the occasional licence of their citizens.

Discussion of totemism and the taboos that it gives rise to, or with which it becomes associated, might appear as a diversion from our main line of argument, but it is in fact essential to it; because of the light their study throws both on the social evolution of prehistoric man and on the origins of religion—which are discussed in a later chapter. Further indirect light comes from an entirely different quarter: the study of primitive sanction and authority.

Self-consciousness creeps up on man unawares. The sacred, the traditional, the established is questioned. Self-consciousness creeps up on mankind; but for the individual it is a sudden experience, an awakening. The more rigid a society, the more violent must be the individual's reaction to his own metamorphosis, and the more appalled must be the rest of the clan at this appearance of revolt. Self-consciousness is the manifestation of superior intelligence. It is an inquiry into the nature of things as well as a recognition of the uniqueness of the self. Its first possessors had no precedent against which to test their new awareness. The odd man in a rigid and disciplined community is outlawed, or rules; the form that self-consciousness took in each instance must have decided the case. Those who were outlawed have no history, nor have the tribes to which they belonged. Those who survived became kings, chiefs, medicine men, witch doctors, and in so doing gave rise to two new phenomena: political authority and religion. The latter in the course of time would gather mankind to its bosom and then fade and give birth to a new star—science.

The king and the medicine man may combine their roles. The same man may be warrior and ruler, reader of portents and weaver of spells; or the roles may be distributed where talent is available. One or both wielded authority of a kind. Both are individual functions, that is to say, functions for individualists. A fissure is made in the equality of men. Men are not born equal, although they may acquire equality, or have equality thrust upon them.

The individual who achieves individuality resorts to the artifices which are essential to his office. Authority lives on its wits, knowing what it has suddenly begun to understand and divining what it pretends to know, or is accredited with knowing.

The tribal chief and the medicine man, by accepting new responsibilities and being unaware of the limitations of their own powers, inevitably lay themselves open to criticism, resentment, hatred and mistrust when they fail; a situation that could never arise in a group which had no chief and took decisions in council. And fail they *must* sometimes, since no one is mentally capable of discriminating between what a king or a magician can reasonably be expected to do, and what they are powerless to bring about or prevent. No one can differentiate, for example, between bringing victory and bringing rain, or can realize that the two things are different in kind.[2] In order to protect themselves from the understandable wrath of their subjects, both kings and magicians surround themselves with an aura of sanctity and a shield of taboos. All taboos in which kingly power is swaddled are explicable either as protections or as punishments inflicted on rulers by subjects, who on many or all occasions are seething with understandable resentment against them.

The priestly and kingly taboos of primitive societies are with us still—divine rights, *lèse-majesté*, paraphernalia and regalia, coronation and anointing and the ennui of court ceremony, procedure and protocol.

In Buckingham Palace no less than in the jungles of New Guinea the origins of primitive societies are available—more or less—for sympathetic study. The resemblances are striking and leave no room for doubt about the origins of kingly authority, and the sources of sorcery, although there are many who still tend to overlook this fact when they attend the Opening of Parliament or the Trooping the Colour.

This chapter is written as a preface to civilization and it attempts to recapture the state of mind of man when on that threshold. How modern the Ancient World seems when we approach it, at last, at the end of such an immense journey. After so breathless and so long a march it seems as well to sum up the opinions of this chapter and so of man's long prehistory.

The totem is the tribal name, given from without. But the name is viewed not as a conventional symbol, but as a personification. This identification adds to and confirms the solidarity of kinship. The kin, not the individual or the family, is the evolutionary unit. The human struggle consists largely in holding communities together in peace, and any device is a good device if it works.

Social evolution can 'set' at this level, and much of our information is drawn from tribes that have never developed beyond the totemic social order.

If it proceeds, and we who write and read these words know that it can and does, it must do so by means of a growth of consciousness. This mutation cannot appear, obviously, in the tribes as a whole, it can, for genetic reasons, only occur in the individual. Equality then begins to give place to diversity. Exceptional men appear who question or even break traditions. They may become nothing more than chiefs or medicine men, but in exceptional circumstances, when a tribe is presented with a new challenge, some would rise to the occasion, and they and their kin would profit by it. The challenge, according to what we know of the genesis of civilization, was probably a climatic one—encroaching desert, invading cold, dessication. A response is made. Leadership is given. Such men are different; they are bene- factors sometimes, but they expect their rewards. The self- conscious man makes claims on the society which he saves. He is acquisitive and his intelligence has created new tech- niques, so his desires do not go unanswered. To satisfy his needs he creates a law—a law which he gives. The law becomes custom and the customs are called taboos. To enforce the law the observance of taboos becomes a sacred, tribal duty. Those who break them have to be punished, otherwise the breaker would tempt others to follow his example. The more universal and the more adamant the taboo, the more violent and the more general must be the desire that it is designed to frustrate.

There is, of course, no question of tribal chief or magician being aware of what was happening to him. His mind was opening and leading him apart. These changes took their measured course through the millennia that preceded history. They did not follow in regular or logical succession. Evolu- tion advances in leaps and bounds and draws to a gradual, or comes to a sudden halt, and the process is taken on and up elsewhere. Many societies—most societies—never attained anything remotely resembling civilization, and some of them are with us still in remote backwaters. The challenges presented to them were too few, too severe or too mild, and their isolation immunized them from the shock of conquest or the contrast of ideas. It is permissible to believe that some peoples—even most peoples—would never achieve civilization however long they were left unmolested to pursue their tribal purposes. The answer to that problem we shall never know, for the forces of civilization are moving in and closing around the last citadels of totemic society. All we can do is to pursue the course of those societies who met and overcame certain challenges, and who with marvellous energy laid the foundations of the world we live and move in today.

11 Mind, Ancient

History is a shadow cast by the moving mind of man. Politics and economics, crafts, arts and sciences, constitutions, codes and campaigns are only reflections. They are mirror-images projected and precipitated as the shape of man's thought alters.

Gerald Heard, *Man the Master*.[1]

MAN WAS A HUNTER and a fisher and when his food supply moved he moved with it. He was a beast of prey and where his prey led he followed. His movements were precipitate or casual according to whether his environment changed abruptly and demanded a sudden decampment, or was stable and allowed him to settle for a time in cave or clearing. There were no towns or villages. He grew nothing and had no domestic animals; and so no bread, no milk, no cheese, no butter, egg or hen. He ate what he killed and what was edible and grew at hand.

A mere 10,000 years ago the world was like that and no man anywhere moved who knew any other life than this. And those wild fathers of us all, what did they make after a thousand million years of biological evolution? Fires, shelters of wattle and grass, tools and weapons of stone and bone, and paintings with refined exactitude; paintings of their prey executed in the deep interiors of their caves—made to invoke their food. Is their earnest, brilliant representational art a clue to their minds? Minds? Unselfconscious mind working on two levels: the submerged unconscious and the conscious; the immediate, the perceptual and the incipient conceptual, growing, accumulating by steady accretion, unknown, unrecognized, unidentified by their owners over the millennia.

One day by careful sifting we may know for certain what

occurred. Now we can only grope and clutch here and there scattered straws of clues, and interpolate by observation, excavation, interpretation, analogy and finally self-analysis, following the faint traces of man's beginnings in the long-buried strata of our own minds.

About 7,000 years ago a change occurred—violent, it seems, by the time-scale by which until now we have been measuring. Upon this change all that has happened since—the whole of history—is firmly and squarely based. Based and dependent but not entirely derived, for two other steps of comparable importance have been taken by man since: one by the Greeks in ancient, and the other by the people of Europe in modern times—to these we shall return.

We know what happened 7,000 years ago, but we can only guess at why it happened then; for opportunities and stimuli lie about or offer provocation, and men pass them by or pick them up and turn them over and to account. They may stare him, for eons unnoticed, in the face; then one day, one year, he sees and is moved. His mind is struck; curiosity, inquiry, experiment follow.

Great changes are not initiated, our historical knowledge informs us, by crowds, although they are caught up and materialized by them. We do not of course, resolve the problem of original thought by tracking it down and accrediting it to a few. This is an observation, not an explanation. But the observation puts the explanation that much more within our grasp.

Man along with all other animals is constantly being faced with new challenges; to overcome one is to create another. The only way that animals can overcome theirs is by the process of biological evolution—physical adaptation. This means that favourable mutations must occur and be exploited, or that favourable recessive genes must have been accumulated and are therefore available for use. Such adaptations are inevitably slow and the nature or duration of the challenge may not allow them to function – may be too complex or too fleeting. The challenge, the chance, may go by. To offset the sluggishness of biological evolution animals have usually one advantage over man: they are shorter lived and more prolific, and more offspring more frequently produced, leads to a faster turnover of generations and so achieves faster physical adaptation.

But man's *élan vital* had gone to his head, so naturally enough it was only in his mind that responses could be made. It was there, therefore, that they occurred. This brings us a little nearer the truth, but it only points the direction without indicating the destination.

In response, then, to a challenge, which had existed un-accepted for millions of years, man began to make revolutionary discoveries; and the greatest among them, because fraught with the most far-reaching consequences, was the discovery that it was possible to raise crops; to grow food, to co-operate with nature, in fact to cultivate.

No agriculture: no civilization. The impetus, the thrust that it gave is derived from the discipline and the stability it imposes upon those who practise it. The domestication of animals for the meat and the milk that they provide does not put an end to nomadism. On the contrary, it may perpetuate it, for animals that are herded and domesticated become their masters' masters. Man instead of wandering in search of food for himself and his kind, wanders in search of food for his herds and his flocks. His quest continues at one remove only from his belly.

The wild grasses, ancestral to our cereals, which provided man with his first bread, make comparable demands. They cannot be grown and harvested repeatedly on the same land without exhausting the soil. In their wild state they are either not harvested, in which case they seed themselves and the soil receives back what it has yielded and more; or they are grazed, in which case the soil receives in return animal droppings which manure the earth and compensate for the loss of its natural produce. In either case the balance between takings and leavings is not upset.

Man did not of course know about this. Agronomy is a modern science, imperfectly understood and still less perfectly practised. The exhaustion of soil is a great nuisance and devices to overcome it are usually harmful. The first tentative experiments in agriculture must have led, even on virgin soil, after a few years, to the exhaustion of the soil in those areas in which it was practised. Agriculture had therefore to be abandoned, or the cultivators had to move to fresh fields and virgin land, and start all over again clearing and turning the earth with hoes and mattocks of flint and wood and bone. The advantage and pleasure to be drawn from the cultivation of the soil must have seemed questionable.

Those tribes who combined cattle-raising with agriculture must eventually have noticed that manure nourishes soil. When this discovery was made the need to move periodically and go in search of virgin land disappeared. Man could settle. The basis of civilization is settlement. It might then be deduced, with a perfectly straight face, that civilization is founded on manure. It might have been true but in fact it is not. Civilization is not based on manure; it is based on mud, as a glance at any map of the world, however general, will show.

As we observed at the end of the last chapter, our civilization is directly descended from the civilizations of four alluvial river valleys: of Egypt, the Nile; of Sumeria, the Tigris–Euphrates; of India, the Indus; and of China, the Yellow River. Civilizations arose successively in that order, between the fifth and the third millennia B.C. It seems more likely that the ideas on which they are based spread from West to East rather than that they appeared independently. It is moreover probable that by 2000 B.C. all these centres were on a comparable footing and that there was regular commerce between them.

All four regions had, of course, something basic in common: they were all subject to flooding when the seasonal rains, or melting snow at their sources, reached the plains. Flooding is disastrous or beneficial depending upon the measures taken to control it. It is perilous to live beside a great river that rises and swells and spreads and washes all before it; that can shift its course by a hundred miles and leave total desolation in its wake. It is also profitable, for a swollen river carries alluvium suspended in its torrent, which it spreads without human intervention neatly and evenly over the land it inundates and so renews. In those four river valleys certain peoples accepted the challenge and met the danger in recognition of the advantages that might accrue. Mud not manure was their fertilizer. They tamed the rivers and so harnessed the mud. As a result, a food surplus was produced which, among other things, released a part of the community from the drudgery of agriculture. They were also enabled—they were obliged—to settle. Settlement and surpluses are conditions of civilization. Permanence and security mean leisure and leisure means time for reflection and perception. Man had reached a destination, a destination that presented a recurrent challenge. The same places and the same objects repeatedly presented provoke thought.

All rivers rather obviously provide water, some also provide fertility; if they provide both, in an area which would otherwise be arid owing to the absence of rainfall, then the situation is pregnant with possibilities. A problem is presented which if resolved will give enormous rewards. The problem is, of course, how to irrigate; how to gain all the advantages of watering and fertilizing without the dangers of flooding; how to ensure that the land shall be drowned periodically but not its inhabitants. As we know, the problem was solved; solved by technique and, more importantly, by communal effort. Irrigation, the canalization of flood waters, was the first considerable co-operative effort man ever sponsored. By primitive standards the areas involved were enormous. Territorial and social barriers had to be sacrificed in the interests of so great an undertaking. The civilizations of Egypt and Babylon, of India and China came into being because of the silt that was spread over all or over parts of their lands, and because the mind of man recognized its value, envisaged its control and above all else broke with tribal tradition and combined to control it.

There are many hundreds of rivers in the world. The fact that among them all only these four produced civilizations begs an explanation. The geography and climate of the regions in which they flowed provides the clue. A small river valley can be the territory of a hunting group. A large river valley which has a moderate rainfall does not need an irrigation system. Rivers large and small which do not flood and run a disciplined course cannot, with primitive techniques, be harnessed. The four alluvial civilizations of which we are speaking presented a perfectly balanced challenge: the areas they covered were too large to be held tribally; they flooded, they had low rainfalls. The nature of the challenge produced a response which broke the grip that tribal totemic society had taken on mankind. Sovereignty had to be sacrificed to a larger interest. Those who refused the challenge have preserved to this day the societies they so loyally and lovingly cherished.[2]

But genius and nonconformity of mind, which is budding self-consciousness, was rare and progress without it was not possible. In a small, tight, traditionalist society nonconformity has few and perilous outlets for its expression. The larger communities brought into being by the four alluvial civilizations created agglomerations in which mind had more freedom and more scope, and where shrewd comparisons could be made and ideas and objects be put in wider circulation.

The difficulties involved in taming great rivers in flood and of distributing their waters regularly over prescribed areas are immense. As the solutions became more efficiently applied and the areas under irrigation more extensive, a dissolution of tribal barriers must have occurred. The stages are unknown to us and may well for ever remain so. What we do know is that by the fourth millennium the process of federation in Egypt had gone far, for by 3200 B.C., the unification of the Kingdoms of the Upper and Lower Nile was achieved. The men who had overcome the technical difficulties must have been called upon either to rule what they had created, or to play vizier to the pharaoh. The solution of the practical problem demanded long-term practical control. Political power of a magnitude and of a kind previously unknown to the world had been created.

We have not landed in one jump from totemic tribe to modern technocracy. The men who effectively brought into being these centralized powers were men of their time who carried over with them into their new positions of power and office all the trappings and superstitions of tribal society. There was no revolution in that sphere. On the contrary the divinity of power gathered force with a new imperial status: kingship, removed by geographical extension from the common gaze and endowed thereby with mystery and exclusiveness; and kingship gorged with wealth for which it could find no better use than to apply to its own glorification, became invisible, mighty, unapproachable and unfamiliar. The mass pursued its unrecorded way, now serving an unknowable priest-king in place of a divine yet homely chieftain.

The challenge had been met; the appropriate response had been made. Man had at last, in certain parts of the world, made permanent settlements and put an end to tribal exclusiveness and absoluteness. The men who achieved this revolution and the men who harvested the power that it created brought with them into office little that would recommend itself to a modern humanitarian. They were self-conscious men—some of them—that is to say, that they were conscious of themselves and analytic of other persons and things within their environment. For, as we have already noted, self-consciousness manifests itself as self-interest to at least the initial detriment of the community. The absolute authority assumed by the new rulers bears this out: they gave their loyalty firstly and lastly to themselves.

This problem—the problem of egotism in a world that could survive only on a foundation of co-operation—would not have been felt at first. For co-operation had in fact been achieved at the lower levels of society—from the peasants' point of view. For the rest, men achieved power either by inheritance or merit, rising to positions of authority or patronage, clustering round their kind in priesthood or bureaucracy. Talent was rare and the positions few in number. The vast mass lived on the land as before, and the extent of the land under irrigation firmly decided the extent of the land under unified political control. Each of these states was in the precise grip of a single unified purpose and economy— the settled cultivation of a uniformly fertilized river basin.

The individual users of the communally constructed canals shared the benefits and the drawbacks. They had lost tribal membership and gained political servitude. Surrounded by desert or mountains the peasant had become a prisoner of the system he had helped to create. His holding could be whipped from under him if he failed to please. Land began to pass out of communal ownership and into the hands of the sovereign lord. To have was to hold on sufferance, not as a right.

The alluvial empires were laboratories in which peoples who had made great renunciations for a supposedly better way of life were committed to the working out of the consequences of their decisions. The regularity of their lives, their sowings and reapings, the routine of their work, the permanence of their entire environment and the monotony of the climate lulled them into an acceptance of continuity and unchangeableness. Their world stood still. And so they built to last, in a way that no migrant people would ever have had the incentive to envisage. Planning not improvisation was the key to success, which involves a change of mental outlook of a revolutionary kind. The camper is in a hurry, pressed to turn to account whatever lies at hand and suffices for his temporary needs. The settled peasant, on the other hand, is stimulated to devise new methods which will make his work endure. In brief, there is every inducement to develop conceptual thought. Impulses are stayed and reflection leads to invention. The consequences of actions are weighed before they are attempted. So were evolved new weapons and tools, houses of baked mud or clay and stone, pots for carrying water or storing wine and oil; food was preserved in deep cool places; cattle were reared and fabrics woven of cotton and silk. The acquisition of belongings had begun. There was no money. Men shared, made and bartered.

Technical advance was painfully slow by modern standards. But it is to be expected that it should have been so, for man had only just come into a new social, settled inheritance; moreover, talent was drawn—as it still is—away from the fields to the cities, and out of the cities up to the court and the temple. With the birth of empire came the establishment of an Establishment.

Rulers must, in their own interests, provide places for mind in evolution. Brains deprived of opportunities are resentful and turn to rend or threaten authority that denies them scope and peaceful outlet. There is no reason to believe that an antique Machiavelli had ever lived and thought this out. Self-consciousness was a slowly rising tide, and agricultural supply was in excess of demand: these were the two salient features of the alluvial empires. The rulers employed the surplus in buying abroad or in building at home. In short they converted the peasant surplus into trinkets and tombs, temples, palaces and works of art. Both courses created a demand for administrative and artistic talent. An intelligentsia was called into being; restricted in numbers and under royal patronage. It was expected to obey and to serve, not to invent.

The alluvial valleys—from Egypt to the Far East—produced food and almost nothing else: wheat and barley, millet and rice, and with the disappearance of game from the swamps that had been drained came the rearing of cattle and the keeping of sheep and goats, hens and pigs. Food in such quantities supported unprecedentedly large populations, and a surplus accumulated. When this was used to buy abroad, international trade was born and so civilization spread. The very nature, geographic and climatic, of these riverine empires ordained that they must lack certain essential materials. Their needs brought them into touch with less civilized peoples, and to those from whom they bought they offered in exchange food and food for thought. Thus, finally, they created not only their own lands but, indirectly, others. They provided the bases upon which we have been building ever since, for they achieved a maturity when history was still young. What they gave out in the form of ideas was used and turned to good account; what they kept has been destroyed, century by century, by the robbing, burning hand of man or effaced by the wind lifting and shifting and piling the desert sands.

Commerce and conquest, rarely curiosity, stimulated travel and exchange of techniques, politics and ideas. Throughout the second millennium B.C., the two empires of the Near East came into increasing contact with each other, and their influence spread throughout the Eastern Mediterranean. Egypt's isolation through rigid natural frontiers gave her a longer lease of life, only interrupted and enriched by the Hyksos invasion. The Sumerian, the Indic and the Sinic civilizations were in touch and exposed to perpetual menace from the north. Centralized power and a submerged peasantry restricted domestic economy and stimulated little inquiry. Speculation had not come yet. Civilization was static and man knew neither whence he had come nor whither he was going. Ancient history is long by our standards, and even modern man, with less excuse, is slow to envisage change, although he is living in a world of perpetual revolution.

In the ancient world most men saw no recordable change within their lifetimes; they were born into and died in a world which must have given, in all its details, the appearance of eternal repetition, as regular and monotonous from the beginning to the end of time as the rising and the setting of the sun and the ebb and the flow of rivers.

With rare exceptions, where a man was born there he lived and died, and in his father's steps he worked and followed. A small middle class served king and priest. In Egypt the prerogative of immortality percolated slowly downwards, indicative—since it was costly—of a growing middle class with a higher standard of living. But advance in this direction was limited and trifling. The economy was not monied.[3] Peasants belonged to large 'households'—as in Russia until the Middle Ages—which supplied all their needs and contributed to the imperial exchequer. There was no shopping except by barter, and the domestic economy was stable because it did not exist.

All of these states were circumscribed by mountains, seas or deserts and were totally preoccupied with their alluvial entities. They had no possibility of, or no interest in expansion; and decentralization, which would have stimulated local initiative, was stamped out since it was viewed as a threat to the authority and the revenues of the king. The enormous effort and the imaginative grasp that had brought about the cultivation of these areas led the system once achieved to stagnation. The success of the ventures and the monotony and sufficiency they created, led to a set way of living and thinking. The civilizations of India and China were geographically isolated; the civilizations of Egypt and Sumer were favoured by their proximity to the Mediterranean, which was neither too large nor too small, neither too rough nor too smooth; and whose northern and southern coasts were climatically sufficiently alike to entice those with venturesome spirits to colonize and trade. Within themselves Egypt certainly, and Sumeria probably, had no possibility of further advance. Progress could only be achieved by other peoples able to turn to good account the great but mouldering traditions that the ancient civilizations had accumulated so laboriously and stored for so long.

About the middle of the second millennium B.C., a

Volkerwanderung occurred which affected Europe and Asia from the Atlantic to the China Sea: the Indus valley was overrun; a Hittite empire was established in Turkestan; the movement spread into Greece and Italy and westwards into Iberia, Gaul and Britain. In all probability it was brought about by a change of climate: desiccation in certain areas, afforestation of steppe in others. Some of the advancing tribes encountered the northern outposts of Mediterranean civilization—notably in Asia Minor, Greece (Mycenae), and Crete. They conquered, absorbed and were absorbed.

When these immigrant peoples came into touch with civilization in Asia and on the fringes of the Eastern Mediterranean, they encountered something that was completely foreign to them. To conjure up an image of them we must throw our minds back 3,000 years from the historical juncture we have reached so far in this chapter, to a time when the alluvial empire of Egypt was still forming. Their culture was neolithic. They were tribal and totemic, and their law was based on kinship and the taboos that adhered to it. Knowing next to nothing of their antecedents, we can only make assumptions from their known reactions to the situations with which their migrations confronted them. They were evidently sufficiently intelligent peoples to have been profoundly affected by the sight of civilization in action. They were shocked into the recognition of a way of life that bore little or no resemblance to their own. Towns they had never seen, houses of brick or stone they had never constructed, metal they had never smelted, agriculture they had never practised, ships and pots and woven clothes they had never before encountered. By these things they were seduced, but not humiliated. They succeeded in fusing their virility with the sweets and elegance of civilized life. They became aware of a different way of life which contradicted their cherished traditions. They accepted the best and discarded the rest. The Heroic Age began.

In the Heroic period the king is a warrior-king and he is not divine. Untrammelled individualism is the *Zeitgeist*. The windows of self-consciousness are thrown open and those who are capable of seeing through them are dazzled by the prospects that the vision offers. Tribal customs and taboos and the laws of kinship are questioned. The invaders, accustomed to roving the wilds and annihilating whoever and whatever opposes them, are brought up short when they find themselves masters of property which is too valuable to destroy; too useful not to be appropriated. They were absorbed into the organizations that they had conquered. Man's concupiscence overcame his destructiveness. Self-consciousness so long held by the alluvial empires in cold storage was, by a strange conjunction of circumstances, about to engulf the world with a torrent; its ripples still disturb the image of history even now— 3,500 years later.

The Heroic Age is of particular significance, since it is the mental and historical link between the halted growth of self-consciousness in the alluvial empires and its full flowering in the age of the city state. Mind is in transition. Transitions are short and violent and, juxtaposed between enduring states of society and mind, are easily lost to sight. We found, naturally, the same situation in animal evolution where links are few and rare and therefore often missing.

The Heroic Age is the age of individualism. It is an age of honour, prowess and vengeance, of personal affront, of 'face' and of sacrifice of oneself for oneself. The age is not peculiar to Greece, but since it is through Greece that the main stream of civilization runs, it is to the Heroic Age in the Aegean that we are drawn for example and precept. The Heroic Age is, however, peculiar to Europe.[4]

The hero of the Heroic Age is violent, barbaric and expressive of a persistent, insistent attitude of mind—his new-born individualism. He is great because he is dynamic and because he bears within himself evolutionary possibilities which, in fact, by his aid will be brought to fruition. He is destructive and absurd because he is puffed up with pride and, having just discovered himself, all else in the world sinks into insignificance when compared with his self-evaluation. Self-consciousness is raw when it first appears; its maturing we shall follow throughout history and see its transformation. It infected the Romans who constructed an empire with it. It drove the Northmen all over Europe and the Mediterranean. It fathered chivalry and the Crusades. It set in motion the Renaissance and the Reformation. It was the driving force behind the Industrial Revolution, and it found a new opening exactly suited to its spirit in the Age of Discovery.

The hero is obsessed with his new discovery—himself. He is a man of action of course, for in action the self finds a total outlet. He pursues his individualism to its logical conclusion; having rid himself of his tribal loyalty, he confers it upon himself. Previously he contributed his part to a group, now he contributes everything to himself. Self-loyalty is called honour. The hero addresses his problems to himself; from that soliloquy he derives his values and finds sanction for his behaviour. Man usurps the role of God; and posterity, in recognition of the service thus rendered, turns its gods into heroes. The metamorphosis is complete. The gods of the Greeks and the God of the Old Testament are characters taken straight out of the Heroic Age. Nothing could exemplify better the spirit of that age than those gods whom men created in their own image and honoured; for to worship such gods was at one remove only from self-glorification.

The hero found heroic outlet for his dynamic individualism in wars, composed of series of battles, in which a few self-important individuals engaged in personal combat. Armies were unknown or if known not used; the common soldier was a spectator. The hero singled out his opponent and struck. Honour was at stake, not defeat or victory. Men did not recognize that the issue of the struggle had any meaning other than this. The hero would desert his comrades if his honour had been slighted and his conduct would be understood and approved.

Heroes and their bands of followers have no future. They destroy others of their kind, and others of their kind destroy them. In spite of this they set an indelible mark on the world. Their courage and their dynamism is admired, emulated and envied. Society always seems— quite wrongly as it turns out, in view of their numbers— at their mercy, but in spite of them society survives. It survives, is strengthened and becomes something else, for the world in which they struggled did not lend itself physically to the kind of political unity that was *de rigueur* in the alluvial empires; nor would such men find in such systems an outlet for their energetic self-interest. But along the coasts of the Aegean they set up, or there were set up individual city states. And the city state becomes a political expression of the hero, inheriting his virile individualism and turning it to account. For the world is not made of heroes, although heroes of one kind or another more or less make the world, however abominable in themselves they may often be.

The city state was in fact obviously suited to the circumstances and environment of the Mediterranean peoples. Its structure lends itself to imaginative and flexible treatment. Each city state was a stage on which the chronic individualist was able to act with the certainty of an audience. The cities being numerous, they provided a multitude of various possibilities and openings for experiment among the demagogically, the tyrannically and the plutocratically inclined. Each was a unit large enough to give weight and substance to its claim to be playing an historic role, yet small enough to give each citizen a chance to feel personally concerned with the status and policy of his state. The phenomenon had such value and persistence that it was revived in Europe during the Renaissance and persisted in Italy, Western Germany and the Baltic until the nineteenth century.

Its chief value, the chief contribution it made to the evolution of mind, lay in its providing a unit of civilization from which no free man was excluded and to which all were drawn into participation. The city state was an invention of individualism and as such gave ample scope for its development. The alluvial empires that had indirectly fathered it were priest-king despotisms. Absolute power was served by the absolutely powerless. The Neolithic peoples, Etruscan, Achaean and Dorian, who had by migrating south and west occupied the Northern Mediterranean seaboard, knew nothing of Egypt or Babylon, and it would not have been in accordance with their natures or their mental powers to give credit to, or conceive of states which suppressed or ignored individual expression. The nascent city states absorbed the knowledge and inherited the commercial enterprises set up by the peoples they conquered, and fused them with their own views on personal freedom. The city states of Greece, and the colonies modelled on this political principle, from Gaul to Asia Minor, were the seemingly inevitable result of such a fusion of ideas in such an environment; creviced by the sea and creased by the mountains into geographically natural units.

City states do not automatically produce genius, but evidently and understandably they do produce an environment in which genius can flourish, and in which men of a lesser stature can find expression. In them the eccentric finds a theatre in which he can act out the part he fancies for himself, even if it leads to his own destruction. Then, as the Heroic Age ends, the vanished heroes reappear as gods, or the gods as vanished heroes. Those who emulate them on a new social and intellectual level have an honoured precedent and popular support.

The Greek, and more particularly the Athenian contribution to civilization has, so far as one can compare such things, no equal. It is much easier to explain why it should have happened then and there than to explain why it should have happened at all. In response to this problem, all that can be said is that the human brain is capable of seemingly unlimited expansion, and that if expansion takes place in a direction which offers opportunities of yet further development, then mental evolution is quickened. Mental evolution, like physical evolution, is a maze wherein almost all the turnings are wrong turnings. Every advance, therefore, is accompanied, followed and preceded by innumerable halts and reverses. When a break-through is achieved then posterity is set the problem of accounting for it.

The fact remains that the city states were a product and extension of man's mental attitude at that time. In Greece it was regarded as the only possible political unit worthy of a civilized man's consideration. Until very recently such a view had much to recommend it, as we shall see when we come to discuss the Renaissance. The city state is an expression of the growth of self-consciousness, that is to say, of individualism, its outward active manifestation.[5]

It is egocentric and aggressive and so much in love with itself that, refusing to face up to its own death, it elaborates an after-life to convince itself of its own survival. It can express itself violently and presumptuously as well as nobly. Its weakness as well as its strength revealed itself very soon after it was born; the city state tempered its self-destructiveness. It has alternately been on a short and a long rein ever since.

Nothing perhaps demonstrates more clearly the character and quality of a people than the way they spend their leisure. There could, then, be no more convincing evidence of the intellectual stature of the average Greek citizen than the character and quality of the plays that were staged in his theatres. We know from them how thoroughly the ideal of self-consciousness had permeated all ranks of Athenian society. To reflect for a moment upon the Roman arena and the Greek theatre and hold them balanced in the mind's eye is to set the comparative value of these two civilizations in perfect focus.

Because we are now in the midst of history and therefore in chronological touch, we must not expect to pursue the growth of mind with regular beat and rhythm. In none of the spheres of its activities does evolution march with a steady tread. Biological evolution is spasmodic, and only discernible at all because we can study its processes over vast stretches of time. The superficial short-term view is that human nature does not change; the long-term view is that human nature does nothing else. It dawdles, it explodes and it backslides, but it is never still.

The genius of the Greek mind is not hard to describe. We can refer to its dynamism, its spirit of inquiry, its unbiased search after truth, its speculative character, its scientific approach, its reliance upon exact observation as opposed to superstition and hearsay, its insistence upon the pre-eminent importance of the human will. We could say all that and more, and with comparatively minor qualifications all these descriptions would be true and fitting and acceptable. And all that can be condensed into one explanation, for until the foundation of the Greek city states self-consciousness was a rare, errant, even a destructive phenomenon; but with their development there came into being a number of societies composed of self-conscious people: governed by them, adorned by them, peopled by them. For to begin to realize one's own individuality is to begin to analyse oneself, and self-analysis is the first step towards the objective analysis of all things. When man begins to study himself he begins to study the whole world, for self-knowledge has no frontiers.

The Greeks had the most profound disrespect for their large and antique neighbours, and not without reason, for the contemporary empires of Hither Asia changed hands but changed in no other respect. Priests and kings or priest-kings ruled subject peoples who never appear to have questioned the source of authority or the manner of its administration. In Egypt life in this world was regarded as an inglorious prelude to life in another. In neither Western Asia nor Africa was there originality of thought or the formulation of any general concepts.

In Babylon, where an efficient method of mathematical notation had been devised, no general laws, mathematical or astronomical, were ever attempted let alone achieved. Specific examples were worked out, memorized and taught, but no deductions were made from them and exceptions were ignored not explored.

In Egypt during the Archaic Period (3200–2660 B.C.), there were signs of a changed mental outlook evidenced by two exact literary works; one theological, the other medical, but they had no successors. Similarly the classical and unexceptional literature of the Middle Kingdom (2080–1640 B.C.) came to an abrupt end and was not developed, but was patiently taught and memorized in Egyptian schools for centuries to follow. Finally, in the middle of the fourteenth century B.C. the Pharoah Akhenaten attempted to break the power of Thebes and establish monotheism, but his reforms did not survive his death and none of his successors followed his example.

In Egypt there was no challenge to upset the even monotony of government, scenery, flood and seed-time, harvest and climate. In Western Asia great empires followed one another in brutal and sickening succession. The sanction on which each rested was superstition and war.

The riverine civilizations had arisen in response to a need for co-operation to control and distribute the flood waters and to parcel out the land. The clan systems had broken up because they were inadequate social structures for the undertaking of such enterprises. In each case the river basin was eventually unified. Central control was desirable on some levels but not on all. Power, however, once centralized became all-embracing, and the resultant despots were tribal chiefs and medicine men writ large.

The city state, on the other hand, starts off on a different footing. The mass is heroically inclined, and the individual is assumed to be self-conscious. The area of each is small, and news and views travel by word of mouth. Every citizen is in the political current, and his right to be so is a tradition which he is not only permitted but expected to exercise. The techniques of communication were too simple to allow larger units to develop democratically. The temptation, even in small units, to resort to despotism is great, as the Spartan and Athenian Leagues demonstrated. For it is not enough to desire to set up democratic government if the conditions for its establishment do not exist. True democracy is direct democracy, wherein the individual can make the state aware

of his views and do something towards effecting their imple-
mentation. The Greek city states' claim to greatness rests on
the fact that at times and in places they achieved this.

The riverine civilizations never attempted an oligarchical
let alone a democratic form of government. There was no
revolution from below: the slight changes that took place
were the result of adjustments from above. There was no
tradition of nonconformity so that the middle classes, when
they arose, desired nothing more than to ape their betters.
They thereby confirmed the existing regimes by bolstering
them with their imitative snobbery in this life, and by pur-
chasing from corrupt priesthoods tickets of good conduct
into the next.

The continued existence and development of the Hellenic
city states depended on a balance being achieved between
close-knit social cohesion on the one hand, and civic pride,
that is to say, aggressive behaviour towards neighbours on
the other. The Greeks did not find this balance. Their splendid individualism shied at the fence of inter-city unity. They
extroverted their aggressiveness and the result was civil war.
They who had done so much for civilization perished because
they were not prepared to make a further sacrifice for a larger
ideal—to form a League of Hellenic city states. Refusing to
yield a little, they lost all and became an easy, divided prey
to be conquered piecemeal, first by Macedonia and then by
Rome. Throughout the whole vast period of evolution,
physical and organic unity and amalgamation plays the major
role. Unity at each level, molecular, cellular and human is no
sooner established than the next step—a wider organism—
presents itself inexorably as a challenge to be met and
accomplished or denied disastrously, and re-presented
and re-presented until by insistence met and accomplished.

The growth of self-consciousness manifests itself as individualism. Manifests itself, of course, in a myriad forms: war, art, sex, political power, athleticism, commerce. If the individuals are few and the unselfconscious are many there is despotism; if the reverse, there is democracy. The Peloponnesian War broke up the only existing nests of democratic government. Once they had been destroyed their survivors became a lost and forlorn minority in a vast amorphous empire. Their voice was not heard.

Rome picked up the bits and welded them into an empire. The parts held together but they made no pattern and they made no growth. The larger the empire became, the more centralized became the authority in whose hands it lay. The priest-king of the proto-civilizations was re-introduced as a Divine Emperor. Individualism had no outlet outside aristocratic circles and even there most perilously. Rome maintained and used many of the political institutions, including that of the city state, which she found in the conquered territories. But deprived of all real power and initiative, they were governed by collusion with subservient, subsidized aristocratic cliques. Democracy was not permitted because it was unstable, exploratory, uncommitted and therefore unreliable. The Roman aristocracy toyed with the borrowed philosophies of Stoicism and Epicureanism. The dead hand of a vast empire lay over the whole civilized world, from the Atlantic to the Caspian and from the Sahara to the Rhine and the Danube.

The Peloponnesian War had marked the end of a period of growth. The mind of man halted there and foundered, because it had failed to invent a way of developing which could combine the individual responsiveness and responsibility manifested in small groups; with tolerance towards other groups of a like or unlike disposition. The aggressiveness of individualism and its territorial exclusiveness—a relic from our pre-human state, which has already been discussed — was no longer permissible in a world where commerce, in its widest sense, between man and man and state and state became increasingly frequent.

We are still learning about the ramifications of this problem and we are still in its grip. One day it will have to be solved: how to live without being bludgeoned, how to let live without being oppressed by those to whom we accord the same freedom that we demand for ourselves.

Is there a thread of meaning running through the confused events of medieval and modern history? Is individualism the summit of human achievement, and when all men everywhere are fully self-conscious will that be a goal, or is self-consciousness merely a camp on the slopes? If the latter, where does mind go from there? What has mind in store — literally in store? Are there clues to its future evolution? I think so.

12 Mind, Modern

But beyond these special activities a greater bond of sympathy has arisen. This bond is the growth of reverence for that power in virtue of which nature harbours ideal ends, and produces individual beings capable of conscious discrimination of such ends. This reverence is the foundation of the respect for man as man. It thereby secures that liberty of thought and action required for the upward adventure of life on this Earth.

A. N. Whitehead, *Adventures of Ideas.*[1]

NINE HUNDRED YEARS separate the deposition of Romulus Augustulus, the last miserable Emperor of the Western Roman Empire, from the beginning of the Renaissance in Italy: a period comparable with that which separates the Norman Conquest from the present day. Almost twice that length of time elapsed between the Peloponnesian War and the decline of Athens, and the rise to influence and power of her true successor, Florence. Over such considerable stretches of the few paltry thousand years of historical time can the mind of man slither, hover, backslide and dilate.

Florence is to the modern world what Athens was to the ancient. The city states of Northern Italy under her intellectual leadership received the Hellenic tradition and built on its foundations. They had, moreover, a hinterland in the continent of Europe, capable eventually of accepting this combined heritage and converting it again into something new. Northern Italy therefore succeeded where Greece failed; not because of any superior virtue but because of the circumstances of the case.

It is pertinent to the argument of this book to stop and note the quickening pulse of evolution. We now consider 900 years as an immense stretch of time providing a valid perspective and displaying clearly identifiable changes and trends. Yet this is a mere tick of the evolutionary clock by

175

standards of organic evolution, and even by standards of ancient history a thousand years can be contemplated as a whole: from the unification of Egypt, for example, until the end of the Old Kingdom. The tempo of evolution has, in our own day, caught up with the tempo of the life of the individual. We are able to record it as a process. It has become observable and, if we will, governable.

Throughout the centuries of Roman Imperial Government and the Dark and Middle Ages, the ideal of city state government never faded. It was regarded as the supreme expression of political wisdom; a view to which the revival of Greek scholarship lent support. The Roman Empire began as a city state and never wholly lost the habit of thought that such a status imposed. Her empire was an appendage: an amorphous mass of fortuitous and deliberate accretions. Greece had been a colonizing, not an imperial power, whose surplus population fitted itself out and set sail to find land, and found cities resembling, but independent of those they had left. They paid only those respects they chose to the city states whose offshoots they were. The umbilical cord snapped and the relationship was effaced by time. To make a biological simile: the Greeks spread by cell division; the Romans by parasitism. In fact, the city state is analogous to the cell in many ways, and the difficulties of the passage from unicellular to multicellular organisms can be compared with the evolution of nations out of city states, because of the specialization and delegation of authority which such a growth entails. To shed some light on this transformation is one of the objects of this chapter.

The Italians lived surrounded by the ruins of their ancient civilization: a constant reminder of a past which called for explanation and one day would awaken inquiry. In the eleventh century the cities of Northern Italy were already beginning to pass out of the hands of the bishops, and when in the fourteenth century the popes transferred their residence to Avignon, and the German claims to interference in Italian affairs had been frustrated, the stage was set for a new act of the human mind. Thus circumstances connived to give the Italian spirit the opportunity it needed to reach full self-consciousness, momentarily freed from the oppressive powers that had hindered it until then.

The development of civic life was the immediate result, and this provided a stimulating atmosphere for revision. Governments were experimental in form and in method; power came into the hands of men who made no pretence of being divine or even legitimate. And men who have no legitimate claim to the power they have usurped, other than their personal fitness for high office, or their ability to maintain themselves in it, turn not to the nobility whose loyalty is obviously grudging and suspect, but to the middle classes from which they can choose talent and on which they can count more certainly for gratitude. Thus class barriers are broken down and the burgher and noble, patron and artist, can meet on an equal footing and to mutual advantage.

Men were encouraged by this political and social climate to become conscious of their own individuality and so to question objectively what everywhere else in Europe was being taken for granted. For in trans-alpine Europe talent was channelled into the administrative machinery of the Catholic Church. No other organization, no government even, possessed a fraction of its wealth, power or influence. It attracted, therefore, the vast majority of men of intellect and ambition. Having attracted them it moulded them into its likeness. There were no outlets for, and no toleration of individual thinkers. Secular power was hereditary so that legitimacy, not competence was the criterion of value in that field. Domestic politics resolved themselves around the ability of dynasties to establish themselves and produce legitimate heirs. Clerical politics were concerned with the maintenance of the ultimate authority of the Church, which was prepared to go to any lengths to humiliate the secular and uphold its own 'spiritual' power. The grip of the Church was tightened by the numerous clerical administrators drawn into the civil service for lack of any other source available to lay authorities.

These were the problems of trans-alpine Europe before the Renaissance. One needs to be reminded of them, for they were the transitory problems of the age. They are only of historic interest; they do not exist anywhere in the world today. The men of Renaissance Italy began to see the world in a new light, and to ask themselves questions which have not been fully answered yet and may never be.

In the North Italian city states, there was from the beginning of the fourteenth century a strong revival of interest in antiquity. Its works, literary and artistic, came to acquire great value, and immense efforts were made and prices paid to unearth, collect, translate and copy them. This interest was further stimulated by the fall of Constantinople in 1453 and the flight of Greek scholars and spread of Greek learning to the West. A study of the past for its own sake is dilettantism in the twentieth century, but it was vibrant with possibilities in the fourteenth and fifteenth, for it represented a change of mind, a curiosity and a disinterested search for knowledge that until then was extremely rare in the world's history. We who are accustomed to rely upon research and observation find it difficult to project our minds back to a time when knowledge was confused with rhetoric, theology, metaphysics and skill in debate.

A study and therefore an imitation of the past can always

degenerate into scholasticism unless it eventually finds a creative response in the minds of those who study it. For appreciation, however genuine and profound, is not creation, although it may be a necessary preliminary. In fact, in Italy it did find a response, so that at one bound the Dark Ages were obliterated and a new Age of Enlightenment was begun. This mental revolution may, in great part, be due to the fact that classical art, literature and philosophy being pagan, Christianity, which had been the official religion of the Western World for a thousand years, had to meet a challenge which was implicit in all that was rediscovered of the Ancient World. The clash was a stimulus, and one or the other had to be rejected or a new synthesis made.

The classical revival in Northern Italy, which started as a dynamic curiosity in a long-forgotten past, was able to run its course because the city states were free from the traditional restrictions that Church and State normally imposed on their subjects. As the Renaissance matured, however, classical learning was apt to be a brake on further progress, since those who had accepted it most enthusiastically were those who became steeped in it the most thoroughly and were the least prepared to look beyond it. Classical learning had to be imbibed, then questioned and then used as a basis for a fresh advance. Those who failed to make the transition from adoration of the past to a respectful criticism of it are with us still, and are responsible for much that is archaic in the fields of education and politics.

The self-conscious man, aware of himself and his own reflections, comes to regard his convictions or his desires as the sovereign authority and oracle to appeal to and consult in moments of decision. He is irked by dogma, tradition and systems of philosophy when they clash with the pursuit of the ends which his personality has created for him. The dangers inherent in undisciplined self-consciousness are many and obvious, and psychological history may be said, with only slight over-simplification, to be the story of the struggle of self-conscious mind to break loose, and the pre-self-conscious mind to hold it back. For whatever merits ortho-doxy may occasionally possess, it inevitably attracts conform-ing and uncreative minds who from and in their entrenched asylums take their revenge and their ease. The Renaissance is the name given to the cracks that appeared in the ice of a long winter. The credit for making them goes to the North Italian in general, and the Florentine in particular. The ice is still melting. Men were finding themselves again, and finding themselves face to face with a world they had hardly noticed: a world open to discovery and re-creation. They set an example, and the changes that took place in the rest of Europe from the sixteenth century onwards were derived, with few exceptions, from or via this source.

The Italian failed precisely where the Greek had failed before him; inter-state rivalry led to a chronic state of war. Victory of one or the other led to repression and reprisals, never to tolerance or partnership. For although the Italians were aware— as the Greeks had been aware— of a common interest and heritage, and although the need for federation was so pressing in view of the squandering of resources that war entailed, and the tempting prize that, in disunity, they offered to a conqueror, they were incapable of sinking their differences and of yielding a whit of their sovereignty for the sake of peace and their common cause. So at a second vital moment in history, the ancient instinct of territorialism learnt so thoroughly in man's animal past, held him in its grip against his reason. To suggest federation was to be accused of treason. The renaissance of the human mind that had taken place in Italy would first be communicated to the peoples of Europe and there developed; then, three and a half centuries later, it would be recommunicated to Italy, by which time to work for unity was no longer treacherous but patriotic— so man's mind evolves, and so his frontiers, political and intellectual, expand.

The Renaissance had, as we have already seen, been allowed to proceed for various reasons undeterred, and without interference from Pope and Emperor, who had other and more seemingly pressing preoccupations. But at the end of the fifteenth century events elsewhere in Europe brought this isolation to an end. From then on France, Germany and Austria successively and repeatedly invaded Northern Italy to conquer, to exact, to occupy, and unwittingly to learn. Europe came and saw, and admired and imitated the country she despoiled, as Rome had conquered and been beguiled by Greece. Modern history began.

Louis XI of France (1461–83), and Henry VII of England (1485–1509), were able to hand over to their successors the first two nation states that Europe had ever seen. They set a political example that is still being imitated to the utmost corners of Africa and Asia, and whose value was scarcely ever questioned until the advent of international authority in the twentieth century. It is in this context; against the backcloth of nationalism, that the modern mind has evolved.

Until the end of the Middle Ages, the feudal pattern of Europe was the outward and visible sign of an inward conservatism. The seigneur was a landed gentleman with claims and estates, and feudal duties which often overrode political frontiers. Apart from the few towns and university cities men lived in antique drudgery, subscribing for the most part unquestioningly to the lay and clerical formulae to which by immemorial custom they were committed. Free inquiry and the dissemination of information and knowledge of science, art and literature did not exist. Life was bounded by the necessities of the moment, by occasional and traditional distractions and by information orally and by chance transmitted.

In England and France in the fifteenth century this state of affairs began to dissolve. In confirming their Royal Houses on the thrones of England and France, Tudor and Valois had broken the power of the barons, and in so doing had rid in great measure the people of them too. Authority, administration and law were centralized, and men could appeal directly to their king. The great sentimental age of chivalry and jousts and tournaments and troubadours and extravagant vows gave place to realism and a change in the role of politics in the lives and minds of men. History became no less political, but it became more and more social and economic.

Even the universities were watched over, if not governed by the medieval Church, with the result that the field of inquiry was circumscribed; learning was a discipline, not an adventure, and the sources of knowledge were never questioned. Thought was thus restricted to the consideration of orthodox opinion, and to the discovery of further proof of and support for proscribed belief. 'The Schoolmen,' wrote Erasmus, 'are looking in utter darkness for that which has no existence whatever.' The difference between the European mind before and after the Renaissance is not easy to define, but its delineaments are unmistakable to read. For the Renaissance was not simply – nor did it simply lead to – a dissemination of learning; it heralded a critical outlook, an enlargement of consciousness, a change of mind.

Until the Renaissance men were with rare exceptions members of a group: in guild, in court, in church, in village and in fief, but rarely conscious of themselves as persons enjoying the right to be consulted as individuals whose minds might be capable of displaying an understanding, a wisdom or an intuition superior to the group from which by birth they inherited rights and privileges, benefits, loyalty and dues. But the grouping of men into tight categories—however valid in the Dark Ages for personal security—reduces enormously the combinations of possibilities, the functions and interchanges of ideas and inventions. When the world of men becomes separated out so that individuals live by their own right, then the richness, even the extravagance of life, its good and its evil is fully displayed. But for this to happen there must be peace of a kind so that fear and sycophancy may dissolve and the mass, no longer made subservient by fear, may be atomized into individuals who are allowed first to whisper and then to broadcast their private doubts.

In a sense the modern Italian is still a Renaissance figure. His attitude to the Church of Rome is still as ambivalent, and his confused historical sense is a compound of the ancient and the ultra-modern. If he has evolved but slightly during the last five hundred years what is he? And what is the limitation of the Renaissance spirit out of which we have passed with gathering speed into the modern age?

It is a limitation of perspective—of depth. Man discovered himself, and the revelation was both blinding and illuminating, and he pursued it to the extreme. His outlook remained, therefore, geocentric and anthropomorphic, and nature was orderly and static. His ideal was the perfectly rounded individual: worldly, cynical, urbane, complete, and holding within himself a comprehensive understanding of the world in which he lived. The individualism of the Renaissance, and the enlightenment it brought in its train, were circumscribed by ignorance: an ignorance so total that men were blithely unaware of it. The world was a small place: an oasis in a desert of space, and man its complex but comprehending and comprehensible master. The myths of the Old Testament were made to serve as a cosmology, and to tell him all he knew or could ever expect to know about time and space and origins. Being unaware of evolution, he was unaware of the context in which he needed to place himself; for self-consciousness is self-awareness not self-knowledge, although of course it is an essential step in that direction. His individualism was, therefore, by our standards naïve, because it lacked depth and recognition of what lay behind the appearance: the perfectability of a handful of people in a tiny world, born yesterday and ripe for eternity tomorrow. The mirror that man held up to himself distorted his image and puffed him up to more than life size.

The whole of history, from its beginnings until the end of the fifteenth century, has been treated in these pages as being reducible to the growth of self-consciousness. A growth which, owing both to the disequilibrium of historical evidence and the demands of literary compression, has been linked mainly with its political expression. Such a treatment omits more than it can possibly include, but for obvious reasons it has had to serve. However, from the sixteenth century onwards it will serve no longer. For from then until the present day – and presumably for all time – the tempo of mental evolution has increased and will continue to increase in so many different fields, and the evidence for it becomes so overwhelming that it is no longer possible to record it by pin-pointing its periodical political manifestations.

The sixteenth century opened in a formidable atmosphere of change. The nation states of England and France, which were to be the political prototypes for the whole world until at least, it seems, the end of the twentieth century, had been established. Italy, opened up by Charles VIII, was beginning to yield its accumulated wisdom. The invention of printing accompanied by improved techniques of paper manufacture

would soon put an end to the laborious copying of manu-
scripts, and lead to the mass distribution of knowledge and
ignorance in ways which have not yet been exhausted today,
nearly four centuries later.[2] America had been discovered,
and the impetus this gave to further voyages of discovery
would eventually lead to the conquest or colonization of four
continents: Africa, Asia, Australia and America.

Man was no longer circumscribed by the frontiers theological, political and intellectual which had for so long
hedged him in. The thirst for knowledge was prodigious,
and had a broader, more popular basis than had ever before
existed. The stories, and the specimens botanical, zoological
and human that the explorers brought back with them to
Europe, fitted uneasily into the dogma of Special Creation
and Noah's Ark.

The nation states and nationalism are new concepts. The
word 'nationalism' occurred for the first time in England and
on the Continent in the nineteenth century. We are so used
to the concept as a political, economic and social anchorage
that its novelty always comes as something of a surprise. It
touches almost every aspect of our thinking: the territorial
limits it sets, the loyalty it inspires, the administrative unit it
comprises, the barriers against other nations it sets up, the
animosities it nurtures, and the absolute inspiration and the
panacea for all evils, it has become for those peoples who for
one reason or another have been deprived of it: all these
things and more, in a world which is clearly struggling to
free itself from what so many people are still struggling to
achieve.

Nationalism spread in Europe under the banner of freedom
and progress; and in Asia and Africa, in our own day, against
Europe its inventor—the lesson having been well learned by
subject peoples from their conquerors. So that nationalism

has destroyed the empires that nationalism constructed. Nationalism – let it be well noted – has aptly in the twentieth century been given a new name: self-determination. At least that describes exactly what peoples in seeking national status are really doing and really, perhaps, realizing what they are doing.

The growth of nation states in Europe can be attributed to two allied causes: firstly, new inventions and techniques from the fifteenth century onwards enabled government effectively to be exercised over larger areas, and secondly, the rise of a self-conscious middle class demanding self-expression and self-determination.

The nation is an instrument which offers – so people believe – the maximum amount of freedom for individual self-expression and personal security. It is, however, a unit held together as much by hatred of neighbours as by patriotic zeal.

The growth of nationalism illustrates two points constantly reiterated in these pages: firstly, the tendency for matter-mind to form ever larger units, atomic, molecular, cellular and so on, which appears as the creative aspect of evolution; secondly, the hostility of the in-group towards the out-group occasioned by the territorial instinct, which appears as the destructive aspect of evolution. This latter aspect has only recently appeared as destructive, for in the form that evolution has taken on this Planet, territorialism has acted beneficially until historical times.[3]

The individual is obliged to forego a certain measure of his personal freedom in exchange for the advantages that accrue to him as the member of a national grouping. This renunciation of absolute individualism acts as a suppression or repression, according to the circumstances of each case, but it reappears as hostility towards the out-group. If the in-groups and out-groups are classes, there is civil war; if they are nations there is national war. But territorialism is vestigial— and vestiges can be comparatively harmless like appendices, or malignant like frontier disputes. In either case territorialism is atavistic and has no place in the modern world; it must be dragged out into the open and exposed for what it was and is.

To preserve the state, individual aggressiveness is chan- nelled off and diverted—wisely, so long as it exists at all— across the frontier. Hence the inability to tolerate one's neighbour: Athens and Sparta, Hindu and Muslim, Arab and Jew, England and Scotland, Florence and Pisa, France and Germany, and so on ad infinitum throughout history, heal- ing and flaring up. Man, in creating the nation state, spread wider his net of co-operation, but at the same time he created an instrument of enormous power. The nation carries within itself the seed of its own destruction; it can only prevent the germination of that seed by facing up to its existence and acknowledging its origins. There are, of course, signs of this happening in the growth of supra-national authorities, world wide and regional.

Behind the façade of political history, a social and intellec- tual revolution was going on, not always silently. The Renaissance, the Reformation and the Voyages of Discovery contributed in various ways to the enrichment of man's mind, and effected a variety of changes which touched him at every level of his existence: the rise of nation states, the neutraliza- tion of the power of the nobility, the centralization of authority, the growth of democracy, the breaking up of feudal exactions and loyalties, the dissolution of the monas- teries and redistribution of vast ecclesiastical estates, the growth of overseas exploration and empire, the Industrial Revolution, the decline of the political and intellectual in- fluence of the medieval Church, the growth of patriotism and the spread of learning. These and many others were outcrops indicating the presence of richer seams yet to be uncovered. Man was becoming self-conscious on a vast scale, and the awareness of his individuality led him to turn to his personal advantage the new knowledge, inventions and techniques that were so continuously coming to hand. To do this it was necessary for him to exploit his environment. But exploitation is totally destructive—and so, in the long run unprofitable—if unaccompanied by analysis and understanding. When this lesson had been learned, man set his foot firmly on the ladder of science: meticulous observation, the testing of belief against experience, the objective search for truth regardless of what it might lead to, the erosion of faith and magic, and their replacement by reasoned inquiry. Man looked out on to the world with a totally new and utterly insatiable curiosity. He looked out and not in, for a fatal dichotomy between mind and matter had long ago been made.

Political history until the end of the Middle Ages was almost the whole of history;[4] for into politics—and of course into the Church from which politics was inseparable—had been drawn those men who were able to separate themselves out from the mass of mankind. This situation changed with the growth of commerce and industry, and the increasing size and number of towns and universities. A new class appeared neither noble nor peasant, which found a multitude of different outlets demanding individual expression. It was the court that would stagnate and the new middle classes that would demonstrate their individualism outside politics, at first, and then gradually invading that field and relegating priest and king to peripheral and archaic functions.[5]

The difference between medieval and modern mind is no more clearly displayed than in the comparison between scholasticism and modern science. The former relied upon endless debate within the prescribed limits of Christian theology and Aristotelean philosophy; the latter relies upon nothing but observation and experiment. The transition from one to the other was only gradually made, and the scholastic attitude is still a force to be reckoned with. The gradualness of this change—if it can be attributed to a single cause—is due to the greatest single blunder that the mind of Western man has probably ever made: the assumed dualism of mind and matter, an assumption which has a long history. Galileo made the distinction between mind and matter purely as an analytical convenience. His work on matter was arrested by the Church and never completed; Part II, 'mind', was never written. This fatal dichotomy survived at first because the Church was powerful enough to forbid inquiry. The division was perpetuated, almost certainly for the same reason, in Cartesian philosophy. The distinction became traditional. It thus came about that physics was studied and psychology was not. The mind became taboo as a subject of inquiry. The Church kept the meat of mind for itself and threw the bone of matter to the lay dog. Man became an observer who dispassionately dissected the Universe but who never turned his gaze inwards. The eye can see all things except the observer.

Until about a hundred years ago, that is to say after Newton but before Darwin, the Universe was regarded as a machine—inexorable, changeless, regular and capable eventually of being perfectly understood. God was the machine-minder. This latter was of course admitted as an over-belief, that is to say incapable of scientific verification. The world was a watch which God had wound up and kept in repair. But machine-minding is not an important enough function for Godhead, so in addition it was assumed that God functioned within the machine, his creation, through his chosen agent, man. Thereby a dualism was created – from our point of view a cross, an overlapping dualism. The first dualism was mind-matter, the second man-nature.[6] So on the one hand there was the Universe, the nature-machine, and on the other man: the specially favoured creature who had free will and therefore was able to profit from the workings of the machine. Nature was rigid, conforming to its God-given pattern; man only was free, and as he increased his under-standing of nature so was he the better able to reap its fruits.

This was the philosophic theory behind nineteenth-century Liberalism. It depended on the clear-cut distinction between man and machine. Liberalism has not survived.

Darwin destroyed the distinction, for he demonstrated that man had evolved through the workings of the machine and that he was consequently simply a product of it, like the monkey, the lily and the flea. Man fell, and in his fall he brought God down with him; for if man was a product of nature, a late-comer to the world, then he could not be God's special agent. Man was relegated, and God was retired to the insignificant pastime of machine-minding.

There is, of course, as we all now well know, an alternative deduction to be made from the theory of evolution, namely that instead of man being relegated to the level of a piece of machinery, nature might not be a machine at all. And man, instead of being shorn of his mind, was confirmed in it and nature was elevated to a place at the mental table; nature was acquitted of the charge of mindlessness.

In the nineteenth century not only did Darwin and Wallace reveal once and for all time the antiquity of man and his his animal ancestry, but Freud unveiled, among other things, the Unconscious.[7] The relationship between these two 'dis-coveries' did not appear at first sight, either because psycho-logy was an infant and not very esteemed science, or because intrinsic importance of the subject, but also because of the corroborative evidence it supplies.

An exhaustive attempt is not going to be made here to reach a definition of religion. For to define it adequately would entail the enumeration of all its manifestations, and each manifestation in its turn would require analysis. The word is too time-encrusted to be reducible to manageable proportions, so that finally only the individual knows, often without being able to express, what he means by it. The writer however has no way out since he must start his argument somewhere, and the reader is entitled to expect to be told what the writer presumes to be writing about. With this apology over, let the argument begin with the postulate that religion appears to have originated from man's desire to put himself in what he believes to be a proper and profitable relationship with the supernatural powers which are presumed to control all those phenomena he cannot understand. Moreover, in order to make his intention effective, he resorts to the performance of certain rites and/or the repetition of certain words. Such performance or repetition may or may be supplemented by the belief in the need to conform to a determined code of behaviour. It may be said at this stage that mimed religion precedes oral religion, and oral religion precedes mysticism and morality.

The above all too brief definition excludes pure magic, but as it fathered both religion and science and it should therefore be profitable before attacking the subject of religion briefly speaking to survey briefly its magical ancestry. It must of course be understood from the outset that it is not possible to draw a hard and fast line between the two. The edges of religion are blurred with its magical contacts. In approaching phenomena of such immense antiquity it is essential to overcome a natural tendency to view them

of the separate compartment in which mind had been put, or because evolution touches so many—in fact all—fields of activity, that men fastened on its most striking aspect first: organic evolution—physical adaptation.

The Freudian analysis came to be linked much less with theories of evolution than—from the vantage point of half a century later—one would have expected. To us the connection is so obvious, for human evolution is hardly organic at all; it is psychological. It follows, therefore, that a study of man is a study of mind, and to study the mind of man one turns to animal psychology, social anthropology and psycho-analysis. Evolution gave psycho-analysis a general significance to add to its strictly particular, personal one. Perhaps Freud did not see his work in this light. He certainly had a preference for the minutiae of the problems of mind so that his observations were more piercing than sweeping.

One of the reasons, perhaps THE reason why the theory of the origin of man and the existence of the Unconscious were not welded into a new synthesis is because the obvious conclusion was repressed. Man had already made a bold and humiliating concession in admitting to an unmentionable sub-human physical parentage. It was too much to expect him to accept the corollary that his mind also had the same lineage. He repressed THAT obvious conclusion, and since repressions are not conscious, it is only we who, thanks to Freud, can rummage more freely about in our minds and bring to light so stark a fact without blushing.

The Unconscious is not buried so deeply that it cannot be unearthed. The acknowledgment of its existence is the first step, the realization of the sort of things that will be found there is another.

If the barriers that reduce communication between the Unconscious and the Conscious mind can be broken down and their re-erection prevented, man will achieve a new advance. He will thereby make the passage from self-consciousness to self-possession and self-knowledge. He will become not only conscious of his individuality but also of what that individuality consists. He will be helped in this transition by steeping his conscious mind in the circumstances of the long and tortuous history of matter of which his mind is the outcome. In recognizing mind as a cosmic attribute of matter, and in reviewing the immense evolutionary journey it has made, he will find it possible to diagnose his passions and his aggressiveness, his myriad instincts rational and irrational, his taboos, his superstitions, his morality and his aspirations; or, at least, when he thinks of the cell from which he came and of the chromosomes that hold an imprint of the passage of evolution through thousands of millions of years, he will pause in wonder that he knows anything about himself at all.

13 The Evolution of the Gods

As soon as we understand a thing we remove it from the sphere of action.

The Note-books of Samuel

IT IS SAID that men get the governments they
seems a hard saying when one thinks of the gove
are and have been. It seems less hard and at least
that men create gods to suit their convenience,
gods they deserve—and feel they require.

Religion of a kind, if the word is given i
tion, appears to be as old as man. And since
has been a mental and social process, and
organic one, it seems natural to conclude
religion must throw a great deal of light
man. Such a study is made easier by th
usually leave material evidence of their
leave a strong mental imprint which is
no matter what transformations it
matter how anachronistic it may beco
and practices are a great reservoir of
of society, and to trouble its waters

Given then that religion has pl
tinuous role in the life of man ov
thousands of years, it must, if w
cults, reflect to an unusual deg
growth of consciousness and s
has been forming in the previc
on religion is therefore incl

with the more sophisticated instrument of the modern mind. It is necessary to slough off layers of analytical thinking and translate one's mind back to a stage of prehistory, buried for the most part deep in the unconscious, before man was self-conscious, and before he ever considered appealing to reason; to a time before he theorized, and before he assumed or concluded that the law of causation underlay all sequences of events.

Having made this translation in one's own mind, it is possible to observe that primitive peoples would find their total environment a confused picture in which the normal and the abnormal, the commonplace and the mysterious were woven into an inextricable pattern which they made no determined effort to unravel or to read. Man was not then, as we are now, inquisitive beyond the bounds of those problems which pressed for an immediate solution as effecting the survival of his tribe, food, children and defence of his territory. Man did not look for mystery, it was only because mysterious events forced themselves upon his attention that he was induced to contrive explanations. As he became more observant, however, the number of abnormalities in nature multiplied. Events fell into one or other of two categories: they were either natural or supernatural, and with the passage of time and the evolution of mind, the line drawn between the two hardened.

To account for the supernatural, man created a god or gods, and this god or these gods were not in his own image. They were formidable, absolute, tyrannical but sometimes amenable to flattery or purchase. In imputing the incomprehensible to the action of a Supreme Being he made a major hypothesis: man had invented religion. God was the unknown, and whether the unknown was or was not unknowable—and therefore a static or fluctuating quantity—he did not stop to question, and he thereby laid up for future generations of self-conscious men a store of trouble.

No explanation, in the modern sense, was sought for supernatural events. Instead, an interpretation of them was made in the form of a story. These stories are what we call myths, and their antiquity is matched by their significance. They are elaborated over thousands of years of oral transmission, and their origins and meaning get lost in tribal memory. They seep into the Unconscious and there they rest, delicately and unobtrusively, to infect our thoughts and feelings. By the study of myths and their interpretation we lay bare the overgrown and hidden sources of primitive society and, incidentally, our unconscious selves. Primitive peoples who have survived in scattered outposts remote from civilization cannot make these deductions for themselves and are totally uninterested in so seemingly academic a project. For them the myths are facts and analysis is foreign to their nature. Moreover, they make the interpretation of their rites that much more difficult by expressing them in action rather than in words. Language, however ancient it may be, until historical times was probably not a sufficiently delicate or complex vehicle to carry the weight of argument as opposed to narrative. Some myths owe their popularity to their function of reducing the terrifying and inexplicable powers of nature, of God, to an earthly parable or story, and so the sting of fear is taken out of them and the Unknown becomes plausible and not wholly alien and unmindful of man.

Myths 'explain' the supernatural, but apart from the obviously supernatural phenomena of, for example, thunder and lightning, eclipses, earthquakes, volcanic eruptions and phases of the moon, there is another category of events: death, pregnancy, and rain, for example, which are irregular and unpredictable but 'normal'. To ward off or bring about such events man had recourse to magical practices. These magical practices did not involve the creation of a god-hypothesis. Man met the challenge of the normal but unpredictable by mime, by imitation, because by a process of reasoning that we call false analogy, he reached the conclusion that to imitate is to induce. This process of reasoning is matched by an analogous belief that the flesh he ate not only nourished him, but transmitted to him also the vices and virtues possessed by the human being or animal before its demise. It therefore seems reasonable to conclude that magic preceded religion because it attempted to satisfy the most urgent and basic needs of man—before he looked above or around him and asked his first immaterial questions about the nature of the phenomena he feared.

Therefore, there appear to be two categories of events which separately or jointly lie at the base of religion. The first are unpredictable, and man resorts to magic to control them; the second are incomprehensible, and man creates supernatural powers to account for them and he weaves stories—that we call myths—around them for the comfort they give him. But it must be borne in mind that these incipient religious growths are always grafted on to a still more ancient phenomenon: the totem, and the taboos—the distilled wisdom of the tribe that accumulated in the totem's shadow.

Consequently, religion seems to have been constructed out of three quite separate but related attitudes. Firstly, totemism, the sacred embodiment of kinship and the taboos that attached themselves to it; secondly, magic, resorted to in order to induce by imitation a desired effect and thirdly, the god-hypothesis, conjured up in an attempt to account for inexplicable 'supernatural' occurrences. The first, totemism, ensures tribal solidarity; the second, magic, is intended to ensure that the tribe is successful in its undertakings, and the third, the god-hypothesis, allays the tribe's profoundest fears. This socio-religious analysis is not intended to imply that prehistoric man ever resolved custom and cult into component parts, or ever made any attempt to distinguish one from the other. On the contrary, every tribe created its own religion, making a confused pattern woven of the three. Now these three aspects are the scaffolding of religion within which massive and formless edifices have risen to great heights. But within historical times what appears at first sight to be a fourth aspect has been added, which has been gradually transforming the whole structure: the Supreme Being has progressively become less and less violent and malignant and more and more gentle and benign.[2] Morality was re-introduced: society's conscience—the direct descendant of the taboos. Man in civilizing himself, civilized his gods. He could scarcely do less than hand on to them the benefits of his own evolution.

Totemism has been discussed at some length already.[3] It was there established that the totem is the tribal 'flag', emblematic of the unity, solidarity and at-one-ment of its members. This, it was maintained, indicated and gave evidence of a pre-self-conscious stage of mental development. Consciousness was still largely collective, and personality was more a group than an individual characteristic.

But totemism is sacramental, for the sacred emblem, the killing or consumption of which is taboo, is on certain occasions sacramentally killed and eaten by the tribe—all members compulsorily present—in solemn and licentious communion.[4] The magical aspect of this totemic feast lies in a belief—held by false analogy—that by consuming the totem animal each communicant digests and is infected by the qualities that the sacred creature possesses. The feast is sacred in both of the basic meanings of the word: holy and cursed. The communicants mutually confirm their guilt and so their kinship with each other and with the totem: their honoured victim. The tribe apologizes to the totem and laments the sacrifice it is making. Guilt is only redeemed because the act is performed communally. If an individual kills or harms the totem he is expelled, put to death or at least made to confess in order that the whole tribe may not be punished for the crime of one of its members.

If then, as is generally agreed, totemism preceded and gave rise to religion then it is easy to understand how it comes about that religion is basically sacramental and monotheistic, no matter to what extent myth and magic are added and woven into the original fabric.

That then, broadly speaking, defines the situation that existed all over the world—and exists still in isolated areas today—until the cultivation of crops and the domestication of animals brought into being the first civilization in Egypt. This civilization broke the whole pattern of human life, for it was based on a major psychological mutation—the growth of self-consciousness.

As we have already seen, the agglomerate of the Nilotic civilization was achieved through the breaking down of tribal, territorial and social divisions, in order to effect a controlled irrigation system in the valley and the delta of the Nile. What one finds, when the mists surrounding the transition from totemic tribalism to divine kingship have cleared, is an organized religion which can be decoded to reveal the transitional as well as the antecedent condition. The pharaoh has become the personification and inherited the role of all the totems which political unity assimilated. The past, however, is recalled by the retention of one totem—the hawk[5]— which is to be seen in representations of the pharaoh, perched on the shoulder of the divine king or on the throne beside him. But the transition from pure totemism to divine kingship is only one aspect of the socio-religious revolution that heralded such a momentous occasion: the genesis of civilization. Something unique was added, and it is this addition that announces beyond any possibility of dispute the dawn of self-consciousness in man.

It does not occur naturally to man to envisage his gods in human form; a fact that comes always as a surprise to us who regard anthropomorphism as naïve and therefore primitive. It was never a primitive concept, but a concept ushered in with civilization. Moreover, it seems impossible to resist the conclusion that there is a direct connection between the development of self-consciousness in man and his clothing his gods in human form. Man in becoming aware of his uniqueness transfers that uniqueness to the objects of power who represent the Unknown.

In Egypt, where this metamorphosis was naturally first made, we find that while the totems have been assimilated into the cult of the divine pharaoh, the other aspects of religion—the Supreme Being, and the myths that surround him—have been modified considerably to adjust themselves to the shift in the focus of consciousness. The change is illustrated precisely by the myth: Isis, the wife of Osiris, conceives a son, Horus, after the death of her husband, as a result of hovering over his dead body. Osiris, although subsequently resurrected by his son, becomes the judge of the dead—a remote god, reminiscent of the fearful aspects of the primitive Supreme Being. Mother and son, however, in human form are his representatives on Earth. God has been made man. Then to round off the theological picture, the totem and the son of god are condensed into a single theme—the Hawk-god, Horus.[6]

The disintegration of tribal society resulting from the advance of civilization led to a corresponding decline and modification of totemic practices. The rapid evolution of society and the dissolution of traditional beliefs created a religious vacuum; the rise of self-consciousness created a need. The vacuum was filled and the need satisfied by the growth of anthropomorphic religion, which seems to have taken one or other of two clearly defined forms.

The first form has already been illustrated by the Egyptian example—the immaculate conception of Horus achieved by his mother, Isis, as a result of hovering over the dead body of her husband Osiris. Whether other religions were influenced by this Egyptian myth or whether they independently resorted to modified forms of it, we are not in a position to decide. The fact is, however, that in some form or other almost the whole civilized world employed this device in order to bring the impersonal power of the unknown god down to earth in the likeness of man. The reasons for the popularity of this myth are easy to understand, for at one stroke it overcame the god's terrifying remoteness and disinterest in the affairs of man; it invested male and female, mother and son, with divine authority and it provided anthropomorphic points of contact with the divine. The vacuum was filled, for men and women had acquired human deities capable of understanding their terrors, their aspirations and their needs.

The following examples show how widespread this expedient for the personalization of the Supreme Being became. In Persia Zarathustra was posthumously credited with virgin birth. In India the Buddha was alleged to have been similarly conceived after an annunciation. In China Lao-Tzu acquired the same reputation. In Greece Dionysus was presumed to be the offspring of a mortal woman, Semele, and Zeus. It will thus be seen that the same myth was current throughout the Ancient World. Wherever tribalism was supplanted by civilization, two socio-religious changes took place: firstly, totemism disappeared to reappear reduced to a sacrament of a civilized religion and secondly, God the Father yielded pride of place in men's hearts to God the Son, who had lived on Earth, a man among men. And it is he – prophet, philosopher, messiah or seer, not the Father – who gives the New Law to replace the outworn tribal taboos.

But the gods can evolve in a different way: a way that is equally indicative of the rise of self-consciousness. The Supreme Being is humanized and converted into a God of gods, and the totems are humanized and converted into a hierarchy of gods to each of which is delegated certain duties, functions or spheres of action. The Greeks adopted this method. This is a synthesis of all the aspects of religion and obviates the necessity of church, priesthood and sacraments. When the Greeks appear in history they have already discarded their totems and substituted a pantheon. From this distance the gods of the Greeks seem to lack dignity because they overreached themselves in their efforts to ape humanity. Their sole inhuman quality was their immortality, and this was only inhuman because it was not achieved by man, not because it was not devised and desired by him.

The evolution of the Hebrew mind, in so far as it is observable through its religious manifestations, took the first alternative – the humanization of God by the birth of a Son conceived of an earthly mother. That a majority of the Jewish people refused to accept Jesus as their Messiah does not affect the point that by them a Messiah was expected, and by them a Messiah was, in fact, produced. Jesus is unimaginable divorced from his background, as the New Testament is incomprehensible unless read in conjunction with the Old. It is surely not unreasonable to argue that the expectation of a son of god is psychologically equivalent to the birth of one, or that if the Gentiles had not usurped him, the Jews who were too exclusive to share him, might eventually have made him their own[7]

It is difficult to avoid the conclusion that the spread of Christianity was in no small measure due to its being clothed in popular myths that were current throughout the Mediterranean. Added to which was the resounding fact that Jesus was not a legendary character from a remote past, but a truly historical figure whose life and death were recent events capable of unquestionable verification. But rapid growth has its drawbacks for it is accompanied by imperfect understanding, and of course wholesale conversion by royal or imperial fiat is disastrous, for in this way a higher religion is apt to absorb more paganism than the pagans absorb of the higher religion.

However, if that was all there was to be said for Christianity it would not have become a world-wide religion, nor would it have captured and held the loyalty of the dominant and only virile civilization extant today, nearly 2,000 years after the death of Christ. It would presumably have passed the way of Zoroastrianism, Isisism and the Dionysian cults. That it did nothing of the sort is surely to be accounted for by the fact that when all the accumulated myths and sacraments are rubbed off there stands out sharply and brilliantly the incomparable message of the Gospels that pagan accretions have so thoroughly yet so understandably overlaid.

Not only were the Gospels unique, so is the whole body of the Jewish Scriptures, and more particularly the prophetic writings. There was very little morality in religion until the Hebrews put it there, and there is very little morality in it still. By and large religion has not concerned itself with teaching men how to live better lives, but how to bribe the gods to temper the brute forces of nature. The emphasis had always been on propitiating the gods and on influencing them to act beneficially: to bring rain and sun and children and food and death to one's enemies in due season. There are exceptions or rather exceptional sayings which crop up rarely and spasmodically in other than the Jewish Scriptures, which give or hint at injunctions of a moral kind. But the Jews were the first people to change— and so far are the only people to have changed— the whole emphasis of religion from the placation of a brutal god to the love of and obedience to a just one.

Is it justifiable to assume that for that reason Christianity survived the assaults made on it from within and without— because, finally, despite its pagan trappings it has appealed to the best in man and the best of men? For in the long run a religion will stand or fall because of the qualities it inspires, not the quantities of converts to which it can nominally lay claim.

Primitive, pagan versions and myths of the powers behind the creation and functioning of the Universe were added to Christianity as it spread and adapted itself— all too well— to the countries and peoples and climates and cults and superstitions it met in its progress. And these adaptations echoed in the minds of all men, for all men's minds had passed by that way. Nothing is lost it seems, no matter how deeply it may lie buried in the Unconscious, and men seldom trouble to follow back to its source the long river that would reveal to them the spring of their actions.

The myths and the dogmas of the incarnation of gods have been covered at some length here because they seem to provide the most specific example of the methods men adopt to adjust their beliefs to accord with their changing selves. Man could scarcely have done more to emphasize his anthropocentricity than to clothe his gods in human form. Nevertheless the example taken is only one of many; for a study of the evolution of the belief in personal survival and salvation provides evidence of man's growing preoccupation with himself and so the immortality of his ego in one form or another.

When man by degrees brought the Supreme Being down to Earth in human form, he did so in ignorance of his purpose in so doing. Moreover, he did not deprive the Supreme Being of his supremacy—theoretically. Man was capable, by theological casuistry, of maintaining the fiction of monotheism, of continuing to pay the Supreme Being his due, and of satisfying the primeval demands of his Unconscious. But it is difficult to escape the conclusion that Mother and Son had, in fact, assumed in men's hearts a place previously reserved for awe of the Father. Christ was peculiarly fitted for this role, for everything that is known about his life and his teaching commends itself to the highest in man, and by his death he fulfilled the age-old myth of the Redeeming King.

The Supreme Being became a shadow by social if not by orthodox evolution. But what had the Supreme Being always been? He was the Unknown God; what man did not understand he ascribed to Him. But man's knowledge is constantly expanding, and so to return to the quotation from Samuel Butler at the beginning of the chapter: 'As soon as we understand a thing we remove it from the sphere of God's action.'

It seems possible to sum up at this stage of the argument by observing that God first yielded pride of place to his Incarnate Son, and then little by little retreated from one defensive position after another before the accelerating advance of science. Man had created God to explain the inexplicable, but as step by step man increased his knowledge he undermined the foundations of his own creation.

Nothing that is offered here as an explanation of the evolution of the god-hypothesis is intended to imply that science has explained or ever will explain all. Belief, however, in a Supreme Being is difficult when the mysteries in which he is wrapped are unveiled to reveal natural not supernatural origins.

The following extract is pertinent to the whole argument:

In all stages of civilization the popular gods represent the more primitive brutalities of the tribal life. The progress of religion is defined by the denunciation of gods. The Keynote of idolatry is contentment with the prevalent gods.[8]

14 The Conclusion

Freud asked, 'What is the origin and nature of psychic conflict?' The next question is: 'What is not conflict? What is the source and character of organic co-ordination?'

L. L. Whyte, *The Unconscious Before Freud.*

OUR BODIES HAVE made a long journey and so, marching in company with them, have our minds. They arose together inseparably in the most unexpected places; they oscillated in gaseous clouds of embryonic galaxies, they were transmuted by the Sun. They cooled and collected and formed into patterns on our Planet's face. They gathered and swarmed in the primeval oceans and along the shallow shore lines of inland seas. They invaded the lagoons, the swamps, the marshes and the tidal estuaries of long-forgotten rivers. They ventured on to the land: over the stretched prairies and steppes and tundra, and into forests high or stunted. We are stardust tempered to a planetary prescription.

Matter has laboured through a span of time measured as yet without precision. Energy and mind are its functions; the world we see about us its sensual expression. The span is so long that it defies human understanding; the imagination deprived of a comparison is helpless. This deprivation goes largely towards explaining evolution's slow dawning. For how could it have come to pass, without unimaginable leisure, that fish and fowl and elephant's tusk; that wing and leg and heart and eye arose from invisible atoms—each related to the common clay—changing, growing, discarding, elaborating, perfecting? This is not credible. The mind is checked and draws back before a synthesis so bold and a time span so appalling.

207

Reason overcame common sense. No comparable synthesis has ever been, or is ever likely to be made; for at one stroke the whole of nature stood revealed as diversity out of unity in the process of becoming. The world was shaken, and is shaking still, for the implications of evolution have not yet been fully realized or developed, although a century has passed since the publication of *The Origin of Species*, and although some of the greatest minds have spent their lives in the study and elaboration of it. Certain deductions were of course explicit to the theory. Our lineage was revealed stretching back millennium by millennium within the framework of four dimensions; stretching back through ages of ice and ages of tropical heat, through ages temperate and intemperate, through ages of mountain upthrust and levelling plains, through ages during which the geography of the Earth in no way resembled that with which we are familiar. For the Earth has been a desperately unsafe place to rely upon for a home or a hearth or a steady living, and few of our forerunners can have died a natural death in the winter of their lives in a hole in the ground or the bole of a tree.

All that seems not too hard to accept — now. But when man was first asked to face up to his longevity and his ignoble ancestry, he was being asked to make a gesture which was by the standards of those times one of great humility. Submission to so rude a theory was of course neither instantaneous nor universal — the diehards are too obvious to mention. And yet is it more noble to have fallen from grace than to have risen from the beast? Is it not finer to be part of nature, to have risen as it were from the ranks, than to have been superimposed? But the nobility and the fineness and the disgrace are matters of feeling and are of small account when set against the total significance and consequences of our origins. These are taking a long time to make their mark on man and on society. It is one thing to make formal submission to the validity of a theory and quite another to deduce and accept the consequences. The formal acknowledgment may float like driftwood for ever on the surface of the mind's sea, while the making of the deductions is a purposeful act like the building of a boat with craft and crew and ports of call and destination. It is time we built and manned and sailed for the implications of evolution are straight and clear.

This book is a pitifully abbreviated attempt to analyse, from the standpoint of the present state of our knowledge, the total implications of evolutionary theory. And this chapter is a summing up, which does not presume to do more than state the author's own conclusions, and to inquire whether they are not justified in view of what has been written so far. But before these conclusions are enumerated and the end reached, there is one problem that must be broached: the problem of free will. It is interpolated here both because its omission might be interpreted as a deliberate attempt to overlook a popular objection to evolution, and because there is little value in reaching conclusions if we do not consider ourselves free to implement them.

Does the establishment of the theory of evolution—the gradual improvement and adaptation of all species by a process of natural selection—undermine our claim to have free will? When we open the door to evolution do we inevitably let determinism in too?

The answer to that question depends firstly upon what we mean by determinism and free will, and whether we have to choose between the two. The definitions are necessarily involved, and the discussion of the problem—once the definitions are agreed—cannot be approached in a book of this kind in the conventional way. What can be done, however, is to use the evidence gathered together in these pages as a sounding-board and see whether it throws any light on the problem.

We have found a compulsion endemic in matter, which may be dormant for ever or for eons and which can only operate in certain circumstances; in planetary circumstances. Even then it can only operate if the planet provides a favour-able environment for sufficiently long—favourable tempera-ture, favourable atmosphere—given these essentials matter can make headway towards forming more complex patterns. There is, of course, no purpose; there is only response. When the correct response is made, a new line of advance is dis-covered; that line, that road is taken not from choice but because it is the only road open. The situation is precisely the same whether we are speaking of organic or inorganic matter. The world is littered with failures: animal, vegetable and human. They are all dumb reminders of how hard the open road is to find, or rather to strike upon by pure chance. Man *hit* upon the way but not all men, although they might have done if left long enough to their own devices. We shall never know. Is this not what the determinists said long ago—the clattering of simian fingers on the keyboard? Is the pro-pellant agent, native to the smallest particle of matter, the real power, and we the puppets pulled this way and that, seem-ingly compelling, actually compelled? Yes, we are com-pelled: compelled by our antecedent condition. The law of causation is never broken, but since we now know the law, we are able both to hasten its operation and to direct our-selves along the open road without needing to test and pursue to their extremity the myriad culs-de-sac. We have laid bare the direction of evolution. That direction must become our purpose. Is that free will? I do not think so. I do not think the word has any meaning. I do not know whether this qualifies to be called a contribution to the determinist-free will controversy, but I am certain that this is the only sound deduction that can be made from our resources of knowledge on the subject.

We can now turn to the conclusions referred to in an earlier paragraph, and so to the end and to a summary of the argument of this book. The conclusions are many, but it is only to what I consider to be the two main ones that I shall draw brief attention here.

The first is social: the second is personal. The first is a criterion of survival. Darwin's phrase 'The survival of the fittest' stuck. It is, I think, a rather unfortunate phrase because – to avoid being deceptive – it needs defining. As it stands it may be interpreted to mean that health and strength are the standards by which the right to survival are assessed, or it can be regarded as a broken phrase which in full reads 'the survival of the fittest to survive', and that is verging on the tautological. The definition, in evolutionary terms, of fitness to survive both individually and socially is anything but an academic question. The phrase caught on, as it stood, and was welcomed and interpreted – by those of the successful who were happy to profit from and still their consciences by any definition however facile – as meaning that unbridled competition was a fundamental law of nature, and that therefore the poor and destitute were irretrievable, and that those who were neither poor nor destitute were confirmed by nature, and so by God, in their possessions.

The facts are of course otherwise, for a closer inspection of the theory of evolution reveals that the fittest to survive are not those who consider themselves invited to exploit, kill or eat their neighbours – according to their fancy or to current custom – if those neighbours are too weak to retaliate. On the contrary, evolution is creative. One might say, to press the point fully home, that evolution *is* creation, and it shows itself to be a force bent in the direction of co-operation. Co-operation is its passion. We with our thousands of millions of years hindsight can note every major step it took, and every major step was a co-operative step. However jagged may be the graph of evolution the trend is unmistakable, it is in one direction only: it is in the direction of increasing co-operation. The trend is equally evident whether we study random inorganic or eventually purposeful organic growth. The individual plant, animal or man is a vast multitude of cells held in unity by co-operation. The incredibly complicated machinery often breaks down, and the result is disease. But disease is the exception, not the rule or the purpose, and the individual who is this multiplicity in unity struggles against the disease, not with it. Moreover, organisms develop and grow more complex not thanks to disease, but in spite of it. It appears that a certain economic point is reached which is the ideal size for a single composite organism. Bulk demands an extension of the principle of co-operation on an individual level it is true, but there is an upper limit beyond which nutrition and communication become insuperable problems. Great bulk has, of course, many other peripheral disadvantages such as decline in sensitivity, physiological disproportion and lethargy. As we have seen, bulk was tried and failed. The urge towards co-operation found an outlet in a new form; individuals extend themselves by co-operating with each other, and social life is born, long before man appears on the scene.

Social life is naturally restricted at first to pairs and pairing that was periodic. But it was successful and was therefore extended to become continuous and to embrace larger groupings. Every extension of the process was evidently biologically advantageous, with the important proviso that the individual had never to be swamped by the community; the parts are sacrificed to the whole only at the whole's peril. For the whole has no life apart from its members; which is as true, of course, of the individual, as it is true of the community.

With history begins the written record of this growth in co-operation. Tribal society has given way not, as one would have expected, to the small compact city state, but to the Alluvial Empires, which show up now from this distance as a kink in the parabola of our graph. They were a necessary kink because, as we have seen, they discovered a system of agriculture which enabled man to cease his wanderings in search of food and to settle and eat, and so build and think and administer—at a fixed address. The Alluvial Empires interpolated themselves, for that reason between the totemic, food-gathering, hunting tribe and the agricultural and commercial city state. In its turn the city state, through 2,000 years of chequered and interrupted history, exhausts its possibilities as a bio-social unit capable of evolutionary co-operation, and is succeeded by the nation state.

Modern history is a record of the growth of nationalism and of the growth at one remove from it of the realization that nationalism is not enough. It has taken the terrifying antagonisms unleashed during this century in Europe to drive this point home. These two European wars, which became general ones, and, strictly speaking, all European wars since the seventeenth century at least, marked Europe's failure to unite, and are paralleled by the internecine wars between the Italian city states, and the Peloponnesian War, all of which brought to an end the systems they were fought to uphold.

The European failure in our time to unite meant that Europe succeeded in losing world leadership which passed to larger units, and Europe is belatedly trying to regain that leadership by resorting to a form of co-operation which she fought those wars to frustrate. In the meantime, co-operation on an even larger scale — on a planetary scale — is being attempted, and despite opposition from the usual conservative quarters has in fact invaded every field of human activity — politics, economics, health, food, communications, trade, labour, education etc.

Now it is not a flight of the imagination to see the modern trend towards global co-operation as in direct succession to the slow attraction of elementary physical particles; for every link in the chain of succession has been investigated and laid bare. We may, out of a desire to be pessimistic or realistic, wish to draw attention to the forces which make for aggression, competition and disease. These forces all exist to a formidable extent, and there is no intention on my part to overlook their prevalence or minimize their power. They have been in evidence throughout the Planet's story, expressing themselves in the forms of repulsion, incoherence, disintegration and war. But our existence bears witness to the triumph, so far, of co-operation as a principle running with a superior force throughout the whole of nature. Wherever and whenever this force has failed so has the biological or social organism, which applied the contrary force of disintegration, failed with it; thus by its self-destruction leaving the field open again to units pursuing the principle of co-operation.

So this is the challenge of our time, and the consequences, if it is not met, will be so extreme that it cannot be said with certainty whether this Planet, let alone man would ever recover or survive. If it is met, and that is by no means certain, it is my opinion that the successful response will not take the direct form of a spontaneous popular revulsion against nuclear war, or a frontal polemic against nationalism, or even against armaments — although all these may play their part—but an indirect form: by a redirection of human energy and ingenuity, and of the Earth's resources towards the resolution of the greatest problems of our time—over-population, under-nourishment and ignorance. The two latter are largely the result of the former, and since it is surely not the quantity of people alive in the world that should be the gauge of man's success, but the quality of the lives they lead, and since we have by mercy and by science eradicated to a great extent the natural checks on over-production, we must control our own fecundity—having usurped the role of nature in this matter.[1] The other problems—under-nourishment and ignorance—can only be solved provided that the world's population does not increase as rapidly as, or more rapidly than the increase in the production of food and the provision of education. That a progressive decline in food and education per head is unavoidable—unless a radical programme of birth control is regionally and immediately put into effect—does not, however, excuse a lethargic approach towards making what provision we can, however many of us there may be. And this is especially necessary if one views the attempt to solve these problems as a way of redirecting our energies and resources. This redirection could take many forms, and it is only possible to touch upon the most obvious here, and then only because it is naïve to speak of the redirection of something if one has not got at least an idea of the form that that redirection could take. It is therefore suggested that for a start international co-operation should be enlisted, and international agencies empowered to take over both space research and the exploitation and protection of the world's oceans and deserts—which comprise seventy-five per cent of the Earth's surface area—as a scientific adventure and as a source of food.

This is altruism and it is easy to sneer; easy and highly

unscientific. Altruism is not utopian nonsense. It emerged from mind as mind emerged from matter, and unless the whole process of evolution—organic and inorganic—and the whole evolutionary interpretation of history can be proved to be nonsense, then altruism is a force which has operated increasingly and with increasing success in the Universe since the emergence of man. Before then, the Planet never had a purpose unless it was to allow to live what could. Nature was a theatre of atoms lacking a purpose but displaying a trend. Since man came, that trend has been slowly converted into a purpose; nature must accept the rule of its prodigious offspring.

And that prodigious offspring has *himself* to study as well as the Earth to heal. There is the mind to fathom as well as the needs of the mind's body to nourish and protect. The study of evolution provides the key to the solution to both these problems; for every individual begins his life with an endowment, organic and social, which these pages have tried to trace. All but an infinitesimal part of that endowment—that is to say the collective unconscious—activates our thinking without our knowledge or consent. Evolution in laying bare the Planet's story has made the unconscious mind of man available for study. It will, however, be known that much of the unconscious is repressed, and that the breaking down of the barrier that prevents the free passage of mental processes from unconscious to conscious is a matter of extreme difficulty. It will also be known that even when that barrier is breached the interchange may only be temporary. There is no guarantee that the resistances that have been overcome will not re-form—so reluctant do we appear to be to know ourselves. It may be a semantic error to speak of the 'breaking down of resistances', for I do not think that it has yet been established that repressions are barred from the conscious mind. It could be that they are restrained by the absence of any means or channel of communication with the conscious mind; channels which, if they once existed in our pre-human past, may for instance have been erased by social life—by taboos. In which case there is no censor, no mechanism, but a blank, and the problem is to re-establish communications and, once established, to keep them open.

In either case the possibility now exists for man to know himself. In doing so he will have faced up to his long past and drawn the conclusions that its recognition demands. This leads to self-analysis: analysis of one's motives, one's passions and one's nature. Such analysis will enable us not only to perceive with a new clarity our mental and physical actions but also those of our neighbours. It may make us less tolerant of ourselves and more tolerant of others. Analysis is of un-limited interest, but—and I quote again from *The Uncon-scious Before Freud*—'Learn to know yourself by all means, when you feel it necessary, but then turn to something in which you can forget yourself.'

We have already discussed in this chapter those external challenges that face us. Let us turn to them.

Notes

Chapter 1

[1] This is not to say that there are no other sub-atomic particles: there are in fact something like a hundred. Protons, neutrons and electrons are singled out for attention here because when they are banded together within the atom—that is to say when they are *not* free—they are stable.

Nor is this to say that these three particles are elemental. The proton, for instance, is certainly highly complex, having a core surrounded by pions, and free neutrons break up into protons and electrons.

[2] A light year is the distance light travels in a year—six million, million miles.

[3] Only the galaxies nearest to us are not receding. This is due to local gravitational attraction.

Chapter 2

[1] There is nothing unusual about such a supposition. At least half the stars in our galaxy have one or more companion-stars.

[2] The brevity with which these theories are necessarily outlined here might tend to give the impression that they are bows drawn at a venture—mere shots in the dark. Nothing could be further from the truth. The problem of planetary origin has been a battleground of opposing theories for over two hundred years. The two outlined above have therefore been through the fire of criticism. Theories of planetary origin must take into account all existing data regarding distances of the planets from the Sun, the planes of their orbits, their angular momentum, the relative abundance of light and heavy elements, etc. The work and calculations involved are vast. A plausible theory is a tour de force.

[3] The fact that all the larger planets in the solar system have themselves got satellites—Jupiter has eleven 'moons' and Saturn nine—seems to lend further weight to the argument that planets are a universal phenomenon.

[4] This method is already in use. One day, any day, an intelligible pattern of sound may be received and recorded. Then and only then shall we know that mind in some shape or form exists or existed maybe millions of years ago and achieved, within the framework of heaven knows what physical shape, at least a technology comparable to our own.

Chapter 3

[1] The greatest and, to my mind, the most inspiring attribute of science is not its discoveries but the reservations with which it accepts them: its total rejection of dogma. This means that however strong the evidence, the possibility is always upheld that something utterly unexpected, unknown and inconceivable may not

have been taken into account. Dogma is devoid of this integrity and ultimately is worthy of nothing but derision.

Chapter 4

[1] The larger a cell becomes, the greater is its volume in proportion to the area of its surface. Since the surface is the 'mouth' of the cell, large cells would be undernourished. Cell division enables the cell to overcome this difficulty.

[2] There are a few rather rare carnivorous plants. Oddly enough the insects that they capture by the most subtle and ingenious ways are not their sole nourishment or indeed essential for their survival.

Chapter 5

[1] Of course earthbound radio and optical astronomers are continually adding to our knowledge of cosmic theory, i.e. the origins of the Universe, its evolution and its structure. The recently discovered radio and quiet quasars may provide an evolutionary link of the utmost importance. It must be remembered that astronomers are looking back in time as well as out in space.

[2] Of course size of brain is a rough guide to general intelligence.

[3] The geography of the Earth bore, of course, no resemblance to that of the present day. Mountains are thrown up and eroded. Land masses are lifted up and then inundated.

[4] Various theories have been advanced to explain climatic changes in general and ice ages in particular. At the present time the theory which meets with most general approval states that variations in the amount of solar radiation reaching the Earth's surface occur as the result of fluctuations in the Earth's orbit round the sun, and in the inclination of the Earth's axis. When minimum radiation coincides with the existence of high mountain ranges then there will be permanent ice of varying thickness and extent. When this coincidence does not occur there will be variations of temperature and precipitation, but no ice. (*See* Jacquetta Hawkes and Sir L. Woolley, *History of Mankind*, vol. I, pp. 18–25.)

Chapter 6

[1] There are exceptions. Unpaired chromosomes are found in somatic nuclei of parthenogenetically produced males of some animals, e.g. bees; also in spores of some primitive plants: algae and fungi. Paired chromosomes are evolutionarily more advanced.

[2] Bacteria, for instance, are an exception.

[3] Mendel's paper was published in an Austrian horticultural journal in 1868. Its importance was not recognized until 1900.

Chapter 7

[1] James Ussher, Archbishop of Armagh, had painstakingly calculated, after perusal of the Scriptures, that the Trinity had created man on October 4th, 4004 B.C. (at nine o'clock in the morning – G.M.T.).

[2] Or the *Élan vital* of Bergson.

Chapter 8

[1] Bradley, *Patterns of Survival* (Routledge, 1939).
[2] Huxley, *Evolution: the Modern Synthesis.*
[3] Mary Field, J. Valentine Durden and F. Percy Smith, *See How They Grow* (Educational Productions, 1954).

Chapter 9

[1] This is one of the reasons why a host of experiences, generally referred to as extra-sensory perceptions, seem to offer no possibility of explanation.
[2] Sherrington, *Man on His Nature.*

Chapter 10

[1] This is not to say that the change from group-consciousness to self-consciousness was sudden and entire. It seems unlikely that the members of a group were ever without *any* awareness of their own individuality.
[2] There are people living in civilized countries today who pray with great seriousness and sincerity for victory *and* for rain, and can become extremely angry when their prayers are not answered.

Chapter 11

[1] p. 8.
[2] 'On the Upper Nile there dwell today people allied to the oldest Egyptians in appearance, stature, cranial proportions, language and dress. These are ruled by rain-maker magicians or by divine kings who were until recently ritually slain, and the tribes are organized in totemic clans ... It really looks as if among these tribes on the Upper Nile social development has been arrested at a stage that the Egyptians had traversed before their history began.' V. G. Childe, *New Light on the Most Ancient East*, pp. 10–11, and as quoted by A. Toynbee in *A Study of History* (Oxford University Press, 1935).
[3] Small change was unknown until well into the first millennium B.C.
[4] This may be an overstatement. Parts of the Bhagavad-Gita are Heroic and could be interpreted as referring to an oral 'Homeric' tradition dating back to approximately the same period (1500–1000 B.C.) of Indian history.
[5] The Oriental — and more particularly the Indian — passage into self-consciousness developed quite differently. It was passive and introspective and has so far remained so.

Chapter 12

[1] p. 107.
[2] No invention has played so large a role in the modern world as the invention of printing; yet the invention did not make the revolution, the revolution made the invention the important thing it became. Inventions do not effect changes if those who are presented with them do not know how to turn them to account. Printing, the magnetic needle and gunpowder were all invented in China long before they reached or were invented in Europe. But in China they lay dormant — unless a passion for firecrackers can bear the weight of being called a practical application.

[3] See pp. 107–8.

[4] The evolution of domestic architecture is a subtle barometer of the increasing significance of social versus political history.

[5] Priest and king maintain a footing in the modern world precisely because of— not in spite of—their conservatism. They can be deposed, guillotined, beheaded, disestablished. They can abdicate and be exiled, or stay on and be shorn of all power, but the priest-king concept is not so easily and quickly erased from men's minds, and the vast impact they once made has atavistically been preserved.

[6] Since it was believed that mind was confined to man, the overlap was less obvious then than it is now.

[7] This is not intended to imply that Darwin, Wallace and Freud owed little or nothing to predecessors. See L. Eiseley, *Darwin's Century* and L. L. Whyte, *The Unconscious Before Freud*.

Chapter 13

[1] p. 325.

[2] The phrase 'Act of God', however, recalls the primitive association of God with malignancy and cataclysmic disaster.

[3] See p. 142, et seq.

[4] Holy days are still celebrated with this clash of extremes—solemn festivals at which the celebrants eat and drink beyond their capacity and try to lose their inhibitions.

[5] Mention should also be made of Anubis, the jackal-god, and Bast, a goddess with the head of a cat. Neither rival the Hawk in importance. Anubis was the brother of Horus.

[6] An indirect consequence of civilization was of course the rise of a progressively more influential, richer and more powerful priesthood with a vested interest in the maintenance of religious belief at a fixed level.

[7] It is tempting to speculate at this juncture and—of course without a shred of evidence—to ponder over the possibility that St Paul's vision on the road to Damascus was due to his sudden perception of Jesus as the embodiment of the myth: there is reputed to have been a temple to Dionysus at Tarsus.

[8] A. N. Whitehead, *Adventures of Ideas*, p. 19 (Pelican Edition).

Chapter 14

[1] The present world population figure is about 3,000 million. A recent United Nations estimate gives the figure of 6,270 million for the year 2000 (*The Future Growth of World Population*, United Nations Department of Economic and Social Affairs, 1958). At the moment of writing there are at least 1,500 million people living in a state of permanent under-nourishment. At the present rate of increase, this figure will have doubled by the end of this century. Yet some organizations by the ruthless application of a sub-human doctrine, and with total and icy disregard for human suffering, stand four-square against birth control which is patently the only cure—apart from nuclear war.

Bibliography

Ardrey, R., *African Genesis* (Atheneum, 1961)

Barnett, A., *The Human Species* (Norton, 1950)

Barnett, L., *The Universe and Dr. Einstein* (Sloane, 1950)

Bouquet, A. C., *Comparative Religion* (Penguin, 1950; Barnes & Noble, 1961)

Bowra, C. M., *The Greek Experience* (English title, *The Greek Experiment*) (World Pub., 1957)

Bronowski, J., *Science and Human Values* (Harper, 1965)

Buchsbaum, R., *Animals Without Backbones* (University of Chicago Press, 1948)

Burckhardt, J., *The Civilization of the Renaissance in Italy* (N.Y. Graphic, 1952; Harper pap. ed., 1958)

Carrel, A., *Man the Unknown* (Harper rev. ed., 1939)

Carrington, R., *A Guide to Earth History* (New American Library, 1965)

—— *A Million Years of Man* (World Pub., 1963)

Carson, R., *The Sea Around Us* (Oxford University Press rev. ed., 1961)

Childe, V. G., *New Light on the Most Ancient East* (Grove, 1957)

—— *What Happened in History* (Penguin, 1954)

—— *Social Evolution* (Schuman, 1951)

Clark, W. E. Le Gros, *The Antecedents of Man* (Quadrangle Books, 1960)

Cole, S., *The Pre-history of East Africa* (Macmillan, 1963)

Daniel, G., *The Idea of Prehistory* (World Pub., 1963)

Eddington, A. S., *The Nature of the Physical World* (University of Michigan Press pap. ed., 1958)

Eiseley, L., *Darwin's Century* (Doubleday, 1958)

—— *The Immense Journey* (Random House, 1957)

Freud, S., *Totem and Taboo* (Norton, 1952)

Gamow, G., *Biography of the Earth* (Viking, 1941; rev. ed., 1959)

Hoyle, F., *Frontiers of Astronomy* (Harper, 1955)

Huizinga, J., *Men and Ideas* (Meridian, 1959)

Huntington, E., *Mainsprings of Civilization* (Wiley, 1945)

Huxley, J., *Evolution: The Modern Synthesis* (Harper, 1943)

—— *Evolution in Action* (Harper, 1953)

—— (ed.), *The Humanist Frame* (Harper, 1961)

James, E. O., *The Beginnings of Religion* (London: Hutchinson, 1948)

Kalmus, H., *Genetics* (Doubleday rev. ed., 1964)

Keith, A., *A New Theory of Human Evolution* (Philosophical Library, 1949)

Kitto, H. D. F., *The Greeks* (Penguin, 1957)

Kropotkin, P., *Mutual Aid* (Sargent, 1955)

Lévi-Strauss, C., *Totemism* (Beacon, 1963)

Mayr, E., *Animal Species and Evolution* (Harvard University Press, 1963)

Oparin, A. I., *The Origin of Life* (Dover, 1953)

Portmann, A., *Animals as Social Beings* (Viking, 1961)

Romer, A. S., *Man and the Vertebrates* (University of Chicago Press, 1941)

Sherrington, C., *Man on His Nature* (Cambridge University Press, 1951)

Smith, J. M., *The Theory of Evolution* (Penguin, 1958)

Teilhard de Chardin, P., *The Phenomenon of Man* (Harper, 1959)

Toulmin, S. and Goodfield, J., *The Fabric of the Heavens* (Harper, 1962)

—— *Architecture of Matter* (Harper, 1962)

Waddington, C. H., *The Strategy of the Genes* (Hillary, 1964)

—— *The Ethical Animal* (Atheneum, 1960)

Walker, K., *So Great a Mystery* (London: Gollancz, 1958)

Walter, W. G., *The Living Brain* (Norton, 1953)

Washburn, S. L. (ed.), *The Social Life of Early Man* (Aldine, 1961)

Whyte, L. L., *The Unconscious Before Freud* (Basic Books, 1960)

Wolstenholme, G. (ed.), *Man and His Future* (Little, Brown, 1963)